Methuen's Monographs on Biological Subjects
General Editors: G. R. DE BEER, M.A., D.Sc., F.R.S.
and MICHAEL ABERCROMBIE

MENDELISM AND EVOLUTION

MENDELISM
AND EVOLUTION

BY

E. B. FORD, M.A., D.Sc., F.R.S.

READER IN GENETICS, AND UNIVERSITY DEMONSTRATOR
IN ZOOLOGY AND COMPARATIVE ANATOMY, OXFORD

WITH SIX DIAGRAMS

METHUEN & CO. LTD.
36 ESSEX STREET W.C.
LONDON

First Published . . August 27th 1931
Second Edition, Revised . November 1934
Third Edition, Revised . March 1940
Fourth Edition, Revised . August 1945
Fifth Edition . . . 1949

CATALOGUE NO. 4105/U

PRINTED IN GREAT BRITAIN

To
JULIAN HUXLEY

PREFACE

THE publication of the *Origin of Species* in 1859 gave rise to a violent and bitter controversy. When this abated at least one important point had been gained ; it was admitted almost universally that evolution is the key-note of biological study and research. Further, the views of Darwin were on the whole accepted, though they received much subsequent criticism in matters of method and detail. It has, however, been agreed that evolution is dependent upon two factors, variation and inheritance, and that it is brought about by the establishment of certain inherited variations within the species, while others are rejected. The explanation of this process, by means of natural selection, was the triumph of Darwin's work. But he was able to throw far less light on the two fundamental principles on which it depends. He had established the fact that animals and plants vary continually under domestication and that they probably do so in nature ; but the causes of this variability could only be guessed at, and some of the guesses were wrong. Furthermore, the whole subject of inheritance long remained a matter for vague speculation ; its very existence did not receive formal proof until Galton and Pearson developed the study of correlation in the latter part of last century.

To-day the position is very different. The particulate theory of inheritance, known as Mendelism, has been the subject of extensive study during the last thirty

years. The result is that we have now a detailed knowledge of the mechanism of heredity based upon a vast
body of facts, while recent work has given us some
information on the physiological processes involved in
the development of inherited characters. In consequence we have also a far clearer view of the nature
of variation than was possible in Darwin's time, for all
problems of variation and heredity are intimately
related ; together they constitute the science of Genetics.
It is evident, then, that these results are of fundamental
importance in the study of evolution, and their bearing
on certain of the evolutionary problems has been discussed in detail in several works. Outstanding among
these is Dr. R. A. Fisher's valuable and illuminating
treatise on *The Genetical Theory of Natural Selection*
(1930).

In spite of this, there appears to be no book devoted
solely to giving a short survey of the evolutionary
aspect of modern genetics, and the present work is an
attempt to meet this need. Up to now students desir-
ing information on this subject have had either to be
content with the few guarded paragraphs with which
it is commonly dismissed in the text-books, or to review
the whole field for themselves and come to their own
conclusions. The latter is, of course, the ideal method,
far preferable to seeking such help as the present author
can give. But there are many who have not the time,
nor even the opportunity, for such a task, and for them
the following account has been written. To bring it
within the reach of all those interested in evolution,
whether they have made a previous study of genetics
or not, a preliminary chapter has been added in which
the principles of particulate inheritance are briefly
re-stated. It must be emphasized that this is not
intended to provide a complete introduction even to

the elements of the subject ; nothing has been included
unless it is essential for a clear understanding of the
discussions which follow. A knowledge of ordinary
biological terms has been assumed throughout, but these
are defined in the Glossary. As this includes all technical words not explained in the book itself, even those
with no biological training will have little difficulty in
following the arguments here set forth, should they
wish to do so.

That the views expressed in this book can accord
with those of all competent geneticists who may read
it, is unthinkable. The subject is beset with difficulties,
with controversy on matters of interpretation, and with
rival theories. In a work designed to be brief, omissions
are inevitable, and some may be serious. But it is
hoped that a useful purpose may in part be served by
bringing together some pertinent facts rather widely
separated in the literature, and by reviewing a few of
the theories which have been developed in recent years.

I am most grateful to Professor Julian Huxley for
his very valuable advice and for a number of important suggestions. I am also indebted to Professor E. S.
Goodrich for his helpful criticism, and to Mr. G. R. de
Beer for supplying me with some very useful information
and for his kindness in reading the proofs.

E. B. F.

Oxford
May, 1931

PREFACE TO SECOND EDITION

IN the second edition of this book I have made several corrections and additions, and rewritten a few paragraphs. I am greatly indebted to Professor R. A. Fisher for his most valuable criticism. I also wish to express my thanks to Dr. G. R. de Beer for much kind help, and to Dr. J. R. Baker for drawing my attention to several errors which would otherwise have escaped me.

E. B. F.

OXFORD
June, 1934

PREFACE TO THIRD EDITION

NOW that a third edition of this book is required, it has seemed appropriate to revise certain sections of it : for the centres of interest have shifted to some extent since it first appeared. Messrs. Methuen & Co. have therefore kindly allowed me to rewrite the last chapter, and to adjust correspondingly the bibliography and index. Elsewhere I have made only those minor alterations which the advance of knowledge has necessitated ; consequently the first four chapters remain substantially unchanged.

E. B. F.

OXFORD
December, 1939

CONTENTS

MENDELISM AND EVOLUTION

PART I

INTRODUCTION

CHAPTER I

THE PARTICULATE THEORY OF INHERITANCE

1. The Laws of Mendel

THE Particulate Theory of Inheritance is due to the genius of Gregor Mendel, a member, and subsequently Prälat, of the Königskloster at Brünn (now Brno) in Moravia. He communicated the results of his work on heredity to the Brünn Natural History Society in 1865, and they were published in its *Transactions* the following year. It is remarkable that this now famous paper passed unnoticed at the time, for it did not attract attention until 1900, sixteen years after its author's death.

Mendel left his conclusions in the form of two very simple laws. First, that when pure-bred individuals exhibiting a pair of contrasted characters are crossed, the original types separate out in definite proportions in the second filial generation, that is among the grandchildren. This process he called *Segregation*. It makes no difference what may happen in the first generation of the cross. This is made up of hybrid individuals ; one of the two characters may be obscured by the

1

other, or some condition intermediate between them may be found. The essential is that no blending has occurred, as is proved by the recovery of the grand-parental types in half of the next generation, the remainder being again of the hybrid constitution.

Secondly, Mendel asserted that when two or more pairs of contrasted characters are brought into the cross they segregate independently of each other. This principle, known as the law of *Independent Assortment*, has, however, been somewhat modified by subsequent discoveries, as will be described in the section on Linkage.

In Mendel's day the phenomenon of segregation, and the constant numerical ratios in which the different types crystallize out of the hybrid mixture, could not be cor-related with any known mechanism. But in the thirty-five years which elapsed before his results attracted general attention, great advances had been made in cytology. It had become apparent that the hereditary material must be carried in the nucleus of the germ cells, for this is often the only part which the offspring receives from both its parents. And in the nucleus had been found self-perpetuating bodies, the chromosomes, which exist in pairs, whose members, having separated from each other, are recombined at fertilization in a manner well fitted to provide the physical basis of the Mendelian segregation of characters.

This close parallel between the genetic requirements and the facts of cytology was first pointed out by Sutton (1902). Modern work, especially that of the Morgan school, has built up a vast body of facts which make the evidence for the chromosome basis of heredity remarkably complete. It may therefore be of value to give a short account of Mendel's two laws in the light of these discoveries.

2. The Physical Basis of Inheritance

A. **Segregation.** Inherited characters are dependent on the action of certain genetic factors or ' genes '
which control them. These are present in pairs, whose
members are derived the one from the father and
the other from the mother of each bi-sexually produced
individual. The paired genes are carried in paired
bodies, the chromosomes, of which every somatic cell
in the organism has a complete set in its nucleus. The
mature germ cells, however, contain but one member
of each chromosome-pair, consequent upon a process
called ' meiosis ' in which they conjugate, separate, and
pass at random to opposite poles during cell-division,
there to be carried into different cells by the constricting
cytoplasm. The total number of chromosomes, and
therefore of genes, is restored when the gametes, each
carrying half, fuse at fertilization.

The members of each factor-pair are called ' allelomorphs ', and from what has already been said, it is
evident that they are carried in different but *homologous*
chromosomes ; that is, in chromosomes which form one
of the conjugating pairs. At rare intervals the chemical
or physical nature of a gene may change. This process,
called ' gene mutation ', is ultimately responsible for the
fact that the members of allelomorphic pairs may exist
in two or more conditions, giving rise to contrasted
variations in the characters which they produce. A
number of such changes may sometimes occur in the
same gene and so form a series of ' multiple allelomorphs '. Only two of the members of such a series
can, of course, normally be present at the same time.

If the members of an allelomorphic pair are of similar
nature they are said to be ' homozygous ', if dissimilar
' heterozygous '. In the latter event their effect may

be intermediate between that which either produces in
the pure, or homozygous, condition or, more generally,
the presence of one type may obscure the action of
the other. The former is then known as a ' dominant '
and the latter as a ' recessive ' character.

It is evident, however, that whatever the heterozygous effect may be, no blending has occurred. For
owing to meiosis during maturation, the unlike members
of the factor-pair segregate from each other in the
separating chromosomes, to produce germ cells carrying
either one or the other type, thus giving rise to fresh
combinations in the next generation.

An example will make this clear. In natural conditions the eyes of the Amphipod *Gammarus chevreuxi* are
made up of black facets separated from each other by
white pigment. A mutation has however occurred, the
effect of which is to make the facets red instead of
black ; when animals of this type are mated together
they always breed true. If a pure-bred black-eyed
Gammarus is mated with a red-eyed individual, all the
resulting family, which constitute the first filial (F1)
generation, have black eyes. Therefore the black-eyed
condition found in nature is dominant to the red-eyed,
which arose by mutation in the laboratory. When these
F1 animals are interbred, segregation occurs among
their offspring, the second filial (F2) generation, according to the first law of Mendel, for three-quarters of
them have black and one quarter red eyes.

The recessive character has thus been recovered from
the hybrid condition, and such ' extracted recessives '
when mated with similar individuals are permanently
true breeding like their red-eyed grandparent of the
P1, or first-parental, generation. The other grand-
parental type, which breeds true for the black-eyed
character, is also recovered, and in the same proportion,

for it is also found in one quarter of the F2 generation. The remainder, half in all, are heterozygotes similar to the F1 individuals. Consequently they do not breed true but, as before, when interbred one quarter of their offspring have red eyes.

This result is at once intelligible on the chromosome hypothesis. The true breeding black-eyed and red-eyed conditions are each dependent on a pair of allelomorphic factors homozygous for the genes concerned. If the factor for black eyes be represented by R and that for red eyes by r, then each cell of the pure black-eyed animal must contain the factors RR, and of the red-eyed rr. These pairs, being allelomorphic, are situated in homologous chromosomes, and they separate from each other during meiosis when the chromosome number is halved. In consequence, the germ cells of the pure black- and red-eyed types contain only one member of each factor-pair; that is, R and r respectively.

When a black-eyed and a red-eyed *Gammarus* are mated, the original number of chromosomes, which has been halved in the germ cells, is of course restored at fertilization. The character with which we are concerned, facet colour, is now once more represented by a *pair* of factors. But this is a heterozygous pair of the constitution Rr, made up of R from one parent and r from the other. At meiosis, therefore, when the allelomorphs separate again, the germ cells of this, the F1, generation receive either the factors R or r. The chances therefore are equal that either type of ovum may be fertilized by either type of spermatozoon. That is to say, a spermatozoon carrying R may meet an ovum carrying R or r, so giving either the combination RR or Rr; so also may one of the equally numerous r-bearing spermatozoa, giving either the combination

2

Rr or *rr*. Three classes of zygotes, then, are possible, *RR*, *Rr*, and *rr*, in the proportion 1 : 2 : 1.

One quarter of the F2 generation are therefore extracted recessives (*rr*) with red eyes, one quarter extracted dominants (*RR*) with black eyes, and one half heterozygotes (*Rr*). These also have black eyes, since, in this instance, dominance is complete. They are indistinguishable from the homozygous black-eyed class but do not breed true. Black- and red-eyed animals thus appear in a ratio of 3 : 1 in the F2 generation.

This result was obtained by producing heterozygotes and mating them with each other. But it is evident that segregation will also occur if heterozygotes are mated with either of the homozygous types. Such a mating is known as a ' back cross ', for it is produced when the F1 (heterozygous) generation is crossed back to one of the parents, or indeed to any other homozygous individual ; the offspring so obtained are said to constitute the R2 generation.

This may be illustrated from the example already discussed. The heterozygous black-eyed *Gammarus* carry the factor-pair *Rr* and, after maturation, half their germ cells possess the *R* and half the *r* factor. The homozygous red-eyed type is of the constitution *rr* and must produce germ cells all carrying the *r* factor. Therefore, on mating, the chances are equal that a germ cell of the latter kind, necessarily carrying the *r* factor, meets one of the former with either the *R* or the *r* factor. Consequently half the offspring have the constitution *Rr* and half *rr* ; half are black and half red-eyed.

Thus segregation occurs in the generation produced by a back cross, the two contrasted characters appearing in *equal numbers*. It is seen, then, that a ratio of 1 : 1 is characteristic of the R2 generation, just as a ratio of either 1 : 2 : 1 or 3 : 1, depending on whether dominance is imperfect or complete, is characteristic of the F2 generation.

The facts so far described can now be summarized in two diagrams (Figs. 1 and 2).

B. **Independent Assortment.** In his second law Mendel stated that two contrasted characters behave independently of each other when inherited together. From what has so far been said of the mechanism of heredity the truth of this statement must be obvious, so long as the factor-pairs in question are situated in different pairs of chromosomes. In such circumstances their allelomorphs will segregate from each other during meiosis and pass into the germ cells at random.

It is evident that when individuals with two contrasted pairs of characters, each exhibiting complete dominance, are crossed, four types will be produced in the F2 generation. These represent the original distribution of the characters and the two possible recombinations between them. Since each type, considered separately, will appear in a 3 : 1 ratio in this generation, the four will together be present in a combination of two such ratios ; that is to say in a ratio of 9 : 3 : 3 : 1.

To make this plain, we will consider the example of the pair already studied, black (dominant) compared with red facets in the eyes of *Gammarus chevreuxi*, and combine it with another pair of factors of quite similar inheritance carried in different chromosomes. Such are the factors controlling the appearance of white pigment surrounding the facets ; the presence of this pigment, the normal condition, being dominant, and its absence recessive.

If a *Gammarus* pure-bred for the black-with-white characters be mated with one having red facets and no surrounding white pigment, the offspring will receive one member of each of the chromosome pairs carrying

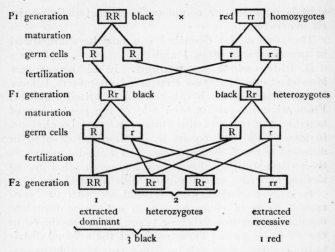

FIG. 1.—Segregation in the second hybrid generation (F2) of a cross between two contrasted characters ; black (dominant) and red facet colour in the eyes of the Amphipod *Gammarus chevreuxi*.

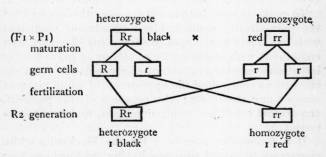

FIG. 2.—A back-cross (heterozygote × homozygote), showing segregation in a 1 : 1 ratio in the resulting (R2) generation. The characters are the same as those in Fig. 1.

these factors, and will be double heterozygotes in constitution. In appearance their eyes will be black with white pigment, for the two dominant characters will, of course, express their effect. Consequent upon the meiosis of this, the F1, generation, each gamete will receive haphazard one member of each chromosome-pair. Four types of gametes are thus formed in equal numbers. For the chances are equal that the factor for the production of the black facets is included with that for the presence or for the absence of the white pigment, so also for the equally numerous factors for the production of red facets.

The chances also are equal that at fertilization any of these four types of gametes formed by one sex meet any of the four formed by the other ; sixteen types of zygotes are thus produced in equal numbers. Of these nine will contain one member at least of each dominant pair, three will be without one dominant type and three without the other, while one will have all its factors recessive.

In order to make these facts quite clear they can now be expressed in two diagrams, Figs. 3 and 4. R and r will again be used for the factors producing black and red facets respectively, while that producing white pigment outside the facets can be represented by W and its recessive allelomorph by w. The members of each factor-pair thus have the same symbols, the capital letter being used for the dominant.

Besides illustrating the facts already described, Fig. 4 demonstrates several other points. It is, for example, to be noticed that only one quarter of the F2 generation would be true breeding if mated to individuals similar to themselves, but this comprises one member of each of the visibly distinct types. Further, individuals homozygous for both dominant and both recessive factors respectively occur only in one-sixteenth of this generation.

The important result obtained by making a back-cross involving two pairs of independently assorting factors will also be apparent. Fig. 3 illustrates that a double heterozygote produces four types of germ cells

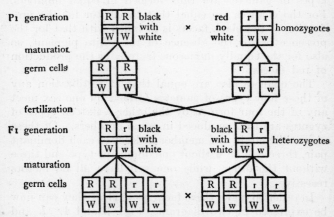

Fig. 3.—Diagram illustrating the formation of four types of germ cells by the individuals of the F1 generation of a cross involving two pairs of independently assorting factors. These are : black, dominant to red, facet-colour, and the presence of white inter-facetury pigment, dominant to its absence, in the eyes of *Gammarus chevreuxi*. The factors in different chromosome-pairs are separated by a double line, those in homologous chromosomes (the two members of the same chromosome-pair) by a single line.

in equal numbers, and it is evident that when both pairs of factors are homozygous only one type of germ cell can arise. A cross between a double heterozygote and a double recessive therefore produces an R2 generation in which the four visibly distinct forms appear *in equal numbers.*

In the present instance the germ cells formed by the double recessive (*rrww*) will all be of the constitution

F1
germ
cells

		RW	Rw	rW	rw
F1 germ cells	RW	**RRWW** black with white	**RRWw** black with white	**RrWW** black with white	**RrWw** black with white
	Rw	**RRWw** black with white	**RRww** black no white	**RrWw** black with white	**Rrww** black no white
	rW	**RrWW** black with white	**RrWw** black with white	**rrWW** red with white	**rrWw** red with white
	rw	**RrWw** black with white	**Rrww** black no white	**rrWw** red with white	**rrww** red no white

F2 generation = 9 black with white, 3 black no white, 3 red with white, 1 red no white.

FIG. 4.—Recombination at fertilization of the F1 germ cells, whose formation is illustrated in Fig. 3. They produce an F2 generation in which four types appear, segregating in a 9 : 3 : 3 : 1 ratio.

rw. The combinations between these and the four types produced by the double heterozygote are illustrated in the lowest horizontal line of Fig. 4.

C. **Linkage.** The number of genetic factors in any individual must be very great, amounting at least to several thousand. It is, however, rare to find a species having more than three or four dozen chromosomes, and often there are much fewer. In *Drosophila melanogaster*, the fruit-fly in which so many genetic problems have been studied, there are four, in *Gammarus chevreuxi* thirteen, and in man twenty-four pairs. It is evident, therefore, that each chromosome must contain many factors. These will be inherited together for, at meiosis, they will pass into the same germ cell without the opportunity of random assortment. This is known as ' linkage '.

If a back-cross is made between two linked factors it is therefore to be expected that only two types will be represented in the R2 generation. The recombination classes will be absent, for free assortment only occurs when the pairs of factors are in different pairs of chromosomes.

It is important to notice that in linkage no association exists between the factors as such, except that they happen to be carried in the same vehicle. Thus two linked homozygous dominants may be brought into a cross by one parent and their recessive allelomorphs by the other. Then, when the F1 generation is back-crossed, the two grand-parental types will appear in R2, in this instance the double dominants and double recessives. If, however, each parent brings in the dominant allelomorphs of one pair and the recessives of the other, on back-crossing to the double heterozygote it is again the grand-parental types which appear ; the double dominant and double recessive classes are now absent. The factors which go into the cross together come out together whichever way they may happen to be assorted.

In order to illustrate linkage an example may be drawn from the work on *Drosophila melanogaster*. The factors for black body-colour (*b*) and curved wings (*c*) are carried in the same chromosomes ; they are recessive to the normal conditions of grey body (*B*) and straight wings (*C*) respectively.

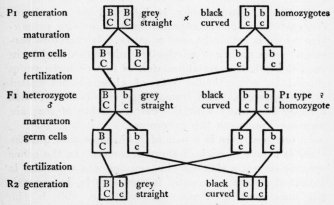

Fig. 5.—A back-cross between two linked factors in *Drosophila melanogaster* ; black body and curved wings, both being recessive to their normal allelomorphs grey body and straight wings. The two factors segregate together without recombination ; compare the formation of four types of germ cells in F1 without linkage illustrated in Fig. 3.

If a pure-bred grey straight-winged fly is mated with one having a black body and curved wings, a double heterozygous F1 generation of grey straight-winged flies is obtained, of which the males produce two types of germ cells only. When mated with double recessive females, to give a back-cross, the two original types appear in equal numbers, and the recombinations between them are not found. This is illustrated in Fig. 5.

Linkage, of course, holds good for all the factors situated in the same pair of chromosomes, however many there may be. Such factors, therefore, are associated together in a 'linkage group'. On the chromosome theory of heredity there can be no more linkage groups in a particular species than there are pairs of chromosomes. Experimental evidence has confirmed this.

D. **Sex-Linkage.** Sex is inherited as a pair of contrasted characters segregating in a definite proportion which is generally near equality. It therefore partakes of the nature of particulate inheritance and is, in fact, dependent upon the action of one or more genes carried in a particular pair of chromosomes called X-chromosomes. The remaining chromosomes, not directly concerned with the determination of sex, are together known as the autosomes.

In one sex there is a pair of X-chromosomes, just as there is a pair of each of the autosomes. In the other sex there is but a single X-chromosome whose partner is almost destitute of genetic factors and is, in general, not concerned with sex determination, this is the Y-chromosome. Sex, then, is dependent upon a quantitative reaction ; two doses of the sex factors carried by the X-chromosomes evoking the development of one of the sexes, while a single dose evokes the development of the other. The former, having similar sex-chromosomes, is known as the homogametic and the latter as the heterogametic sex. It is a highly remarkable fact that the heterogametic sex is in some forms the male, and in others, lepidoptera, the birds, some fishes and amphibia, it is the female.

From what has already been said on the subject of linkage it is to be expected that the X-chromosomes will contain many factors other than those for sex, with which, however, they will necessarily be linked. Such 'sex-linked' factors, then, are inherited relative to sex, unlike those situated in the autosomes.

Fig. 6 shows the inheritance of a sex-linked factor, white-eye colour (*w*) in *Drosophila melanogaster*. It is recessive to the normal red-eyed condition (*W*). When a white-eyed male is mated to a pure-bred red-eyed

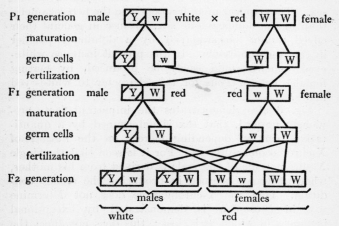

FIG. 6.—A cross involving a sex-lined factor in *Drosophila melanogaster*. A male carrying the recessive factor for white eyes (*w*) is mated to a female carrying its normal allelomorph (*W*) for red eyes. Segregation in a typical 3 : 1 ratio occurs in F2. No white-eyed females appear, though half the males resemble their male grandparent in that they show this character. The Y-chromosomes are shaded, the X-chromosomes are not.

female, all the offspring have red eyes ; the daughters, however, carry the white-eye factor while the sons do not, for they receive their only X-chromosome from their mother. On interbreeding the F1 generation it is found that red and white eyes appear in a typical 3 : 1 ratio in the F2 flies, but they are not distributed at

random between the sexes as the characters previously
considered have been. Half the males, but none of the
females, have white eyes like the male grandparent.
The appearance of the white-eye character is thus linked
with the male sex though inherited through the female.
It should be noticed, however, that the appearance of
recessive sex-linked characters is not confined to one
sex. They appear more frequently in the heterogametic
than in the homogametic sex, because in general their
effect cannot be swamped by a dominant partner
in the Y-chromosome. In the present instance white-
eyed females could easily be produced, by mating
females heterozygous for this character to white-eyed
males.

Fig. 6 also demonstrates the important fact, previously noticed, that sex is determined by a quantitative reaction depending merely on the *number* of
X-chromosomes present. For it is seen that the single
X-chromosome of the male is derived from his mother,
where it was concerned in producing the female condition. That the Y-chromosome does not determine
sex in *Drosophila* is demonstrated by exceptional
instances in which it is lost ; this does not affect the
development of the male.

E. **Crossing - over.** Linkage, however, is not
always complete, for an exchange of substance, and
therefore of genes, may occur between the chromatids
derived from homologous chromosomes during the
prophase of the first meiotic division. This is known
as *Crossing-over*. At this time the chromosomes become
spun out into thin threads (the leptotene stage) which
twist round each other. Subsequently each splits longi-
tudinally, forming a pair of ' chromatids '. The evidence indicates that pairs of chromatids, whose members
are derived from homologous chromosomes, exchange

blocks of material at one or more points. The frequency with which this may occur varies with the environment (temperature affects the process) and with the constitution of the individual. In *Drosophila*, for example, certain genes prevent a breakage occurring in their immediate neighbourhood, while no crossing-over is possible in the males of this genus ; indeed in all forms it appears to be less frequent in the heterogametic than in the homogametic sex. On the other hand, the frequency with which a breakage and interchange may occur between any two factors is constant in the same conditions. It is important very briefly to study crossing-over, and the light which it throws on the mechanism of heredity.

If two individuals, one homozygous for the dominant and the other for the recessive allelomorphs of two pairs of factors, are mated, double heterozygous offspring are produced. It has been pointed out that when these are back-crossed to the double recessive class, then, if the two pairs of factors are in different pairs of chromosomes, free assortment takes place. The two grand-parental types and the two possible recombinations between them all appear in equal numbers.

If, however, the factors are in the same pair of chromosomes, and complete linkage exists, the two grand-parental types only will segregate out. But when crossing-over occurs there appear in addition some individuals belonging to the recombination, or cross-over, classes. In order to estimate the amount of crossing-over, these are added together and expressed as a percentage of the whole. This is known as the ' cross-over value '.

When the cross-over values of three factors situated in the same chromosome are studied, it is found that an important relationship exists between them. For the cross-over value between the factors A and B added to that between B and C is equal to the cross-over value between A and C. This indicates a linear relation between the three factors in question. Numerous tests have been applied to this conclusion, and it has been ascertained that the genes are in fact arranged in linear order along the chromosomes. The closer together any two factors happen to be, the smaller is the chance that crossing-over will take place between them. Thus it comes about that the percentage of crossing-over is a measure of the relative distance of the factors from each other. It has therefore been possible to construct maps showing the order and position of the factors on the chromosomes. Allelomorphic factors are those which lie exactly opposite each other. Thus we arrive at a definition of allelomorphism : *allelomorphic factors are situated at identical loci in homologous chromosomes.*

It has been established that crossing-over does not take place between single factors. Blocks of genes cross over together, as would be expected if, in fact, this phenomenon is due to the twisting of the chromosome threads round each other during the prophase of the first meiosis. It is evident that when two widely separated factors are studied, there is opportunity for crossing-over to occur twice between them, so upsetting the expected cross-over value. If, however, the factors studied are close together, the chances of double crossing-over taking place are small. This possibility is even further decreased by the fact that crossing-over at any locus protects the region for some distance on either side of it from coincident crossing-over ; as would again be anticipated, for intertwining threads have a modal length of twist. For short distances and small cross-over values, therefore, the linear relationship previously indicated between three factors is accurately maintained.

Proofs of the way in which crossing-over occurs and

of the linear order of the genes have been obtained by various methods. A consideration of them is, however, quite outside the scope of this book. Suffice it to say that it has been shown by Plough (1917) that crossing-over actually takes place at the only time when the chromosomes, which may normally be rounded bodies, are spun out into threads and twist round each other. Other recent work, for example that of Painter and Muller (1929), has linked up genetics with cytology in a convincing manner. It is no longer possible to maintain, as has been done quite recently (Russell, 1930), that the factors may be due to the action of the individual chromosomes as a whole. For it has been shown that when a piece of one of the chromosomes breaks away, the action of the factors in the remaining portion is normally unaffected ; while should the missing fragment become attached elsewhere, it carries its own factors with it and they are uninfluenced by their separation from the major part of their chromosome. Another result of this work has been to enable chromosome maps to be made on cytological evidence (Dobzhansky, 1930a). They confirm those based on genetic evidence.

Finally, in order to make the subject of crossing-over quite clear, an example may be given. In *Drosophila melanogaster* the factors for pink eyes and curled wings are recessive to the normal conditions of red eyes and straight wings. If a pure-bred fly with red eyes and straight wings be mated to one with pink eyes and curled wings, all the offspring (F1) will have red eyes and straight wings like their normal parent. When females from such offspring are mated to male flies with pink eyes and curled wings, an R2 generation is obtained consisting of 49 per cent. of flies with red eyes and straight wings, 49 per cent. with pink eyes and curled wings, 1 per cent. with red eyes and curled wings, and 1 per cent. with pink eyes and straight wings. These last two represent the recombination, or cross-over, classes. Added together it is seen that the cross-over value between the pink and curled factors is 2 per cent. Thus they are situated in the same chromosome and at a distance of two units from each other. Had they been in different chromosomes the four classes would have appeared in equal numbers. If, on the other hand, they had been completely linked, as they would have been had the F1 males been mated to double recessive females, only the two grand-parental types would have appeared.

It is to be noticed that in this instance both dominant factors came in from one grandparent and both recessives from the other. At segregation this association was preserved, with rare recombinations. The two dominants and the two recessives thus appear to be coupled together, and such an association is known as *Coupling*. *Repulsion*, on the other hand, is said to occur when the two dominants come in from different grandparents ; this arrangement tends to be preserved at segregation, and the two dominants and the two recessives appear to be repelled from each other. Coupling and repulsion, though at one time regarded as distinct processes, are therefore seen merely to be manifestations of the same phenomenon.

If individuals doubly heterozygous for two linked factors are interbred to produce an F2 generation, instead of being back-crossed, coupling will give rise to an excess of the first and last classes of what with free assortment would be a $9 : 3 : 3 : 1$ ratio. Repulsion would lead to an excess of the two middle terms.

Cross-over values of 50 per cent. cannot be distinguished from free assortment. Factors giving this value would be placed in different linkage groups until a factor situated between them, to which both would of course be linked, chanced to be discovered. For this reason it has sometimes been reported that a species has more linked factors than pairs of chromosomes. This has never been substantiated, for the true condition has always been revealed by a more detailed analysis.

F. **Mutation.** Many meanings have been applied to the term mutation. It is, however, convenient to restrict it to the inception of a heritable variation. This may take the form either of a gene mutation, which is a change in a genetic factor, or of a chromosome abnormality.

Gene mutations, then, are responsible for the fact that allelomorphic factors may exist in two or more conditions ; they are consequently of fundamental importance in heredity and evolution. They are of very rare occurrence, so much so that it is most difficult to estimate their frequency. Even in *Drosophila melanogaster*, of which far greater numbers have been studied than of any other animal, such an estimate is rather untrustworthy, for the number detected will greatly depend upon the skill of the observer. It would seem, however, that a given gene seldom mutates in more than one individual in three hundred thousand : usually more rarely. They appear to be completely localized changes. Mutation at one point in a chromosome is not accompanied by simultaneous mutation at other loci nor even in the allelomorphic factor. It can occur in the body cells, as well as in the germ tract, so giving rise to 'somatic mutation'. This results in a mosaic appearance similar to that sometimes produced in heterozygotes by the dropping out of a chromosome, due to a failure in mitosis. When

3

this occurs in a homozygote it must be attributed to somatic mutation.

Gene mutations can, however, be induced by short-wave radiation from X-rays or radium, and their frequency may be increased at least fifteen or twenty thousand per cent by this means. The rate of increase appears to be proportional to the energy of the dosage absorbed, and is independent of the wave-length (Oliver, 1930). Although the great rarity of mutation in natural conditions throws much doubt on most conclusions based upon its relative frequency, it would seem to be established that some loci are more mutable than others. The greater frequency of gene mutations at the white-eye locus of *Drosophila melanogaster*, as compared with other loci where only a single change has been detected, is certainly statistically significant. Thus there would appear to be a characteristic mutation rate for each locus. On the whole it seems that those loci which mutate most frequently in normal laboratory conditions produce the most mutations when treated with X-rays. It is possible to suppose, therefore, that the artificial induction of mutation is concerned in raising the general level of the mutation rate.

The causes which bring about mutations in normal conditions are at present quite unknown. It can only be stated that the amount of radiation occurring naturally seems insufficient to account for them (Muller and Mott-Smith, 1930). The important question of the nature and frequency of mutations in laboratory conditions as compared with those in the open will be discussed in Chapter III.

The type of change which occurs at gene mutation has been a subject of much controversy. In the past many workers have been led to the conclusion that a

physical loss of material takes place. That gene mutations, however, must often represent chemical changes
rather than physical losses is indicated by the proved
fact of reverse mutation. It is hard to conceive of
mutations occurring in both directions with a frequency
at all comparable to each other if an actual loss were
involved in the original change. It has, however,
been pointed out (Ford, 1930, pp. 561–2) that some
gene mutations may in fact represent physical losses
of material. But these are probably exceptional, and
the evidence for their occurrence is quite other than
that which led to generalizations on this subject in
the past.

The occurrence of chromosome abnormalities may
also lead to hereditary changes. These are to be divided
into two distinct classes: exceptional fragmentation
of the chromosomes themselves, and abnormalities in
the distribution of whole chromosomes.

The first of these types occurs naturally, though
very rarely. It is, however, quite a frequent result
of treatment with X-rays. Portions of chromosomes
may break away and become attached either to the
homologous chromosome (duplication) or to one of
the other chromosomes (translocation), while sections
of a chromosome may be lost, so giving rise to deletion.
Failures in cell-division, on the other hand, lead to polyploidy, in which more than two members of the chromosome-pairs are present ; or to heteroploids in which
either an extra chromosome may be added to the
group or one lost from it. A study of the chromosomes
in allied species indicates that such irregularities have
occurred in nature. It is clear that in certain instances
they have played a part in evolution.

The effect of heteroploidy is generally deleterious since

the genic balance is upset, but a simple multiplication
of the chromosome number is free from this defect.
The forms in which this has occurred are known as
autopolyploids. These are usually fertile with one
another, but not with individuals whose chromosome
number is a different multiple from their own. Thus
they are capable of originating a new stock which may
evolve along its own lines and lead to a specific difference.

The chromosomes of a polyploid may, however, be
derived from two different species (allopolyploidy).
Hybrids between different species should contain the
haploid number of each. They are generally sterile,
since the chromosomes have no identical partners with
which to conjugate during meiosis. If, however,
they double this number, producing an allotetraploid,
each chromosome gains a partner and fertility is restored.
In this way fertile hybrids, sterile with both their
parental forms, may be produced. This is a near
approach to the formation of a new species. It has
occurred under experimental conditions (*e.g.* in *Primula
Kewensis*, the hybrid between *P. floribunda* and *P.
verticillata*), and it has done so in nature (pp. 106–7).

Polyploidy, then, has played a part in the evolution at least of plants. But the changes it initiates are
often considerable, and then they must generally be
disadvantageous (see p. 46). It must be very un-
important in animals, for they are rarely self-fertile
and, furthermore, their mobility and quantitative sex-
determining mechanism will tend to prevent the establishment of this type of mutation.

3. SUMMARY

Mendelism is a particulate theory of inheritance.
Characters are due to the action of pairs of factors,
and these are carried in paired bodies, the chromo-

somes, whose members are derived respectively from the two parents ; they separate from each other again in the germ cells.

The factors may exist in two or more conditions, so producing contrasted characters. When two individuals with such characters are crossed, the original types separate out, or *segregate*, in definite proportions in subsequent generations. Re-combination between the factors is possible, since the pairs are parted from each other in the separating chromosomes and so may be combined afresh at fertilization.

The number of chromosomes is constant in a given species and each contains many factors. The pairs of factors segregate independently of each other if situated in different pairs of chromosomes, if in the same pair they are 'linked' and inherited together. Sex is dependent upon genetic factors carried in a particular pair of chromosomes. They have a quantitative action ; one dose of the sex factors producing one sex and two doses the other. Numerous other factors are carried in the sex chromosomes and hence are linked with sex. In many instances an orderly interchange of material takes place between pairs of chromatids derived from homologous chromosomes. This allows the recombination even of linked factors, which 'cross over' with the substance exchanged from one chromatid to the other. The factors are arranged in linear order on the chromosomes and are situated at definite loci.

Mutation, the inception of a heritable variation, may be due to changes in individual factors, or to fragmentation of the chromosomes or irregularities in their distribution. It is a phenomenon of great rarity, but it can be induced artificially. Almost all heritable variation owes its origin to such mutation.

PART II

MENDELISM AND EVOLUTION

CHAPTER II

HEREDITY AND THE ENVIRONMENT

1. THE EXTERNAL ENVIRONMENT

THE mechanism of heredity has been briefly outlined in the preceding chapter. For this purpose it has been convenient to regard each gene as the inherited basis of a particular character in the adult organism. Yet such a concept as this is but a partial truth, and it is essential to discuss the real relationship of the genes to the characters before arriving at any clear understanding of the nature of variation and of its hereditary control.

One of the most important discoveries bearing upon this problem is the fact that the same genetic factor does not always have the same effect ; for it was early found that the genes interact with the environment. Changes in temperature, in food or in humidity, may all influence the complex action of a gene upon the developmental processes which lead finally to the production of a given character in the adult organism. That this is true is hardly surprising, for we know how great may be the effect of the external environment upon processes of growth and differentiation.

That genetic phenomena are susceptible of exact study is due to the fact that a given gene will always have the same effect in the same environment. Alter the external environment and the effect of the given gene may be changed ; restore it, and the original effect will be recovered.

It is at once evident, then, that variation in any character may be due to two distinct causes ; to changes (mutations or recombinations) in the genes controlling it, or to changes in the environment affecting the action of such genes. Variation of the former type is said to be ' genetic ', of the latter ' environmental '. It is useful to employ corresponding terms to describe the individuals themselves. An organism judged by its genetic constitution is called a ' genotype ' : one judged by its appearance, a ' phenotype '. The phenotype, then, depends upon the expression of the genotype in a given environment. An example will make this clear. We will choose the character already selected as illustrating the simple working of the laws of Mendel ; black as compared with red facets in the eyes of the Amphipod *Gammarus chevreuxi*. In this way it will be easy to trace the connexion between the mechanism and the physiology of inheritance.

In natural conditions the eyes of this animal have black facets. It is viviparous, the young being hatched from the egg in a maternal brood-pouch, from which they are extruded after some days in a fully developed condition. Though minute, they differ but little from the adult. The eyes are fully developed and the facets are of the normal black colour. If, however, the eggs are removed from the brood-pouch and developed artificially outside the mother, it is seen that the facets are at first a clear bright red. But they rapidly darken through shades of brown and chocolate until, at the time when extrusion would normally have occurred, they become black (Ford and Huxley, 1927, pp. 113–14).

Thus when colour first appears in the facets, the eyes of the wild-type *Gammarus* are similar in appearance to those of the red-eyed form already mentioned as having arisen by mutation in the laboratory. But even in the latter the red colour does not always persist. Gradually, after a period of weeks or months, it may darken until, in some old individuals, the facets may be of a deep blackish brown. It has been proved (*ibid.*) that this change is due not to an alteration in the red colouring matter itself, but to a slow deposition of the black pigment (melanin) which is found in the eyes of normal specimens.

We see, then, that the difference between the black- and red-eyed form is due merely to the *rate* at which black pigment is deposited in the facets ; a change occupying a few hours in the former type takes many weeks in the latter. Further, we obtain some insight into the nature of the genetic control of this character. The genes for the black and red facets in the eyes of *Gammarus* simply affect the rate at which a single substance, melanin, is deposited in the eyes. It is probable that such rate-factors, controlling the speed and time of onset of processes in the body, are of very general occurrence (Ford and Huxley, 1927, pp. 126–32 ; *ibid.*, 1929).

But it is evident that environmental conditions, such as temperature and food, which influence the growth of the animal, will also affect a process such as this which depends upon developmental rates. And, in fact, it has been proved (Ford and Huxley, 1927, pp. 124–26 ; 1929, pp. 70–1) that temperature has a direct effect upon eye colour in *Gammarus*. In the red-eyed form melanin is deposited so rapidly at 28° C. that the eye becomes approximately black in twenty days, while at 13° C. only a minute quantity is laid down after many months, and the eye remains bright red. At 10° C. it is even possible so to delay melanin deposition that the facets of the normal black-eyed form are still quite red at extrusion from the brood-pouch. It has also been shown (Ford, 1928) that if growth is delayed either genetically or environmentally, in a red-eyed *Gammarus*, the quantity of melanin produced in a given time has to be shared out over a smaller area in the facets. Therefore, if kept at a high temperature, the genotypically red eye of such an individual can for a time become completely black and indistinguishable from the genotypic black eye of the wild-type animals.

The distinction between these two types of variation will now be plain. A character may vary when the genes controlling it are kept constant and the environment altered, as does the colour of the facets in genotypically red-eyed *Gammarus*, which may be made phenotypically red or black environmentally. It may, on the other hand, be varied genetically by keeping the environment constant and altering the genes which control it, as may be done by appropriate matings, bringing in the black or red factor and keeping the individuals at a low and constant temperature.

In fact, it may be said that all characters are the combined results of genes acting in a given environment. Alter either the genes or the environment and variation may ensue. The genes do not stand for this or that character in the adult organism; it can only be said that in a particular environment they will always have an identical result. Such an assumption is the logical outcome of all that is known of genetic action.

It seems that genes whose action is easily influenced by the environment are found in all groups of animals and plants which have been the subject of genetic research. Two examples out of many may be cited from the work on *Drosophila melanogaster*, as illustrating different types of environmental effects. A single recessive factor causes the reduplication of one or more of the legs. Sometimes only a few joints are affected, but at others all the legs may be doubled even down to the base. This factor only produces an effect at low temperatures. When the flies are reared in an ice chest, normal segregation is obtained in crosses with the wild type, but at higher temperatures, say 23° C., it is quite without effect even in the homozygous condition (Hoge, 1915). Similarly, ' abnormal abdomen ', a semi-dominant sex-linked factor, results in a more or less complete obliteration of the regular banding of the abdomen. This character is fully expressed in cultures obtained from freshly made-up stock bottles. It becomes less pronounced in the flies which hatch later, until, in old cultures, all are completely normal, even the homozygous females. The abnormal effects are, however, once more obtained in full when the offspring of such phenotypically normal but genotypically abnormal flies are reared in a fresh culture medium. It has been found that moisture is the necessary agent for evoking the action of this gene ; when the cultures dry up it can operate no longer. Both changes in temperature and in the acidity of the culture media have been excluded as causative agents (Morgan, 1915). Such instances as these might be greatly multiplied.

Among plants, the interaction of genetic factors with the environment may be illustrated from Barley, in which Collins (1927) detected the unusual condition of a

viable albino. This is due to the action of a single
recessive factor, but it can only produce the completely
albino type when the plants are grown below 6·5° C.,
while above 18° C. they develop the full amount of
chlorophyll and cannot be distinguished from normal
plants. However, instances of the operation of the same
phenomenon are, in reality, constantly provided by the
varied response of plants to growth in different situations. The effects of alterations in soil and climate are
too well known to require illustration, but they demonstrate the reaction of the plants' hereditary outfit to
environmental changes.

It is evident, however, that some characters may
have a fairly wide range of toleration for environmental
change. We cannot in advance predict without experiment that a given alteration in the environment will
affect the action of a particular gene. In fact it is
possible to regard genetic factors as having *characteristic* effects. So much so that in the past many workers
have fallen into the trap of identifying, in some measure,
the genes with the characters they normally produce,
an error which has done much to obscure the interpretation of genetic phenomena.

That such a point of view should be possible is due
to the fact that all organisms have an optimum environment in which they are most efficient. To this they
are often so accurately adapted that it is impossible
for them to live in other surroundings ; while animals,
at any rate, may positively seek out the right conditions,
or maintain them by a physiological control by which
they create a permanent and constant environment
for themselves. It happens, then, that we are generally
studying the action of genes in an environment close
to the optimum ; one which is therefore fairly constant.
So it comes about that the interaction of the genes

with the environment may be by no means evident ; nor can it always be demonstrated, for quite a small departure from optimum conditions is fatal to many organisms.

To take an excellent example. Temperature is one of the most obvious and important of environmental factors ; we have already discussed how it may interact with a gene and affect a character in the adult organism. That each animal has an optimum temperature, which may differ widely in different forms, is a fact too well known to require emphasizing. Some species will tolerate a considerable range of temperature on either side of their optimum, to others a minute departure from it is fatal. Typical of the latter group are the Mammalia, which maintain their temperature permanently at optimum level and consequently, in this respect, live in a constant environment from which they cannot normally be dislodged. Yet we have reason to think that many of the genes in this group only produce the effects known to be characteristic of them because they always operate at this particular temperature. Indeed in one instance at least the change of temperature necessary to influence the character produced by a gene is so small that it can be detected even here.

Himalayan rabbits differ from the wild form by a single factor-pair, the Himalayan colouring being recessive to the ordinary brown agouti. This factor is responsible for the production of a white coat at the Mammalian optimum temperature. At a temperature a few degrees lower, its action is entirely different, for it no longer produces white but black hair. Himalayan rabbits are born uniformally white, for the whole body has been maintained at a high and constant temperature before birth. But subsequently the

extremities, the ears, muzzle and feet, which are subject
to chilling, turn black ; for these parts are cooler than
the rest of the body and this difference is sufficient
totally to alter the effect of the Himalayan factor.
That the darkening of this race is the result of temperature has been proved in the following way. If a
patch of hair be shaved off the back of two Himalayan
rabbits and the one be kept in a warm and the other
in a very cold place, the hair which grows again will
be white in the former environment and black in the
latter (Schultz, 1920 ; Castle, 1924, pp. 218–19).

2. THE INTERNAL ENVIRONMENT

It is seen, then, that the genetic factors interact with
the environment to produce the characters for which
they are responsible. But the environment is not only
external but internal, and by the internal environment
is implied the total effect of the genetic constitution
of the animal. The means by which this can control
the chain of reactions from a particular gene to a
particular character, so as to produce variability, must
now be briefly sketched.

The essential of Mendelian inheritance is its particulate nature. This, of course, refers to the behaviour
of the genes as individual units, it does not refer to
the characters, for a single character is the result of
the interaction of many genes. There are, in fact,
unit factors but not unit characters in heredity.

Factor interaction, then, is a matter of fundamental
importance in the study of genetic action. Its recognition dates from the well-known observations of
Bateson and Punnett (1905 ; and 1906, pp. 11–16)
on comb shape in fowls. These authors found that
the rose and pea combs were each dependent upon a

single factor which behaves as a dominant to the normal single comb. When brought in together they interact to produce a new type of comb called ' walnut ', which is therefore due to the interaction of two factors each having a different and characteristic effect by itself. Instances of this kind are now numerous in the literature of genetics.

Of a slightly different nature are those characters dependent upon the operation of several factors with similar but cumulative effect. Nilsson-Ehle (1909), working on the inheritance of red and white colour in wheat grains, found that red was incompletely dominant in the F1 generation and that all shades appeared in F2, from whitish to a nearly full red. His results led him to formulate the concept of *multiple factors*, which he developed with conspicuous success ; their existence has now been detected in other forms. A simple instance is that of the genes 'Stubble' and 'stubbloid' in *Drosophila melanogaster* recently studied by Dobzhansky (1930b). The former is heterozygous, being lethal as a homozygote, and the latter recessive. They control the same characters and reinforce each other.

The class of 'modifying factors' presents a somewhat different type of factor interaction. Many of these have no detectable effect save in the presence of some particular gene.

Bridges (1919) made a study of a number of such factors which modify the character ' eosin eye '. This depends upon the action of a sex-linked recessive, one of the series of multiple allelomorphs at the white-eye locus ; it changes the red eye of the wild-type *Drosophila* to a yellowish pink, of a somewhat lighter shade in the female than in the male. In the presence of this gene the factor ' cream 2 ' can easily be detected, since it interacts with it to produce a marked lightening in eye colour, which becomes a pale yellow destitute of any trace of pink. In ordinary circumstances, however, " cream 2 " has no visible effect even in the homozygous condition.

' Eosin eye ' has a somewhat lower viability than normal, and it is improbable that it could establish itself in nature. But a striking example of modifying factors operating in natural conditions is to be found in the butterfly *Papilio polytes*, as was demonstrated by Fryer (1913). The female of this insect has three forms. One of these, known as *cyrus*, closely resembles the male, and a dominant factor converts it into the widely different typical form *polytes*. There exists another dominant which is without effect in the *cyrus* constitution. It interacts, however, with the *polytes*-producing factor to give rise to a third distinct form called *romulus*.

These two factors are *sex-controlled*, that is to say they can only produce the characters for which they are responsible in the internal environment provided by one of the sexes. In the other, in this instance the male, they are without effect ; their relationship to sex is therefore of a physiological nature. Such factors may be situated in any of the chromosomes. They are thus to be distinguished from the sex-linked factors (p. 14) whose relation to sex is of a purely mechanical kind, since they are the factors carried in the same chromosome as those for sex and are, in consequence, linked with them. It is, of course, possible for factors to be both sex-linked and sex-controlled.

Essentially similar to the modifying factors is an obscure type of factor interaction, which has been encountered on a number of occasions, and may be illustrated by the work of Wexelsen (1928) on the occurrence of extra spermathecæ in *Drosophila melano-*

gaster. He was able to demonstrate that this peculiar reduplication is due to the combined action of at least three pairs of factors, situated in different chromosomes, each of which is without visible effect by itself.

It is apparent that the factors most convenient for genetic study are those which in the normal environment give rise to some well-marked character. This may in reality be but one of several quite evident effects of the factor in question, but, being the most obvious, it comes to be regarded as the primary one and the others as secondary. That the existence of these secondary effects is in reality a widespread phenomenon is evident from the large and increasing number of instances in which they have been detected. They have on several occasions been the object of special study, notably by Dobzhansky (1927), and they may affect any organs of the body quite independently of the primary character. Thus the factor for white eyes in *Drosophila* is responsible also for a change in the colour in the testis-sheath and for a characteristic alteration in the shape of the spermatheca. The white-eye character is merely selected as being the most convenient indication of the presence of this particular gene.

Even more important for the present purpose is the marked influence of mutations on viability. That this is nearly always of an unfavourable kind will be a matter for discussion in the next chapter. It is at present sufficient to notice its existence. Of the hundreds of mutations which have, for example, been studied in the various *Drosophila* species, scarcely one has been found which does not lower the viability as compared with the wild type, and many are actually lethal as homozygotes. Such a result can hardly ever be accounted for by the nature of any observable struc-

4

tural changes. It indicates that the effects of a gene are far more profound than a study of the visible characters would lead us to suspect. In reality they must include physiological and other reactions which can only be detected by their influence on the general health and vigour of the organism. The almost universal nature of such changes in viability justifies us in assuming that the genes are probably always multiple in their effects.

It is to be noticed that the mere observation that a particular gene has manifold results does not exclude another explanation. Theoretically it is possible that there are in reality as many separate mutations, linked so closely that crossing over between them is virtually impossible, the whole group therefore being inherited together. That such an assumption is not generally tenable can be proved in those instances where the same mutation has occurred more than once. Not only the primary but also the secondary effects have then appeared again. The chances against the simultaneous mutation of several such factors are almost infinitely remote.

The interaction of the genetic factors to form an internal environment will now be apparent. It is evident that the effect produced by any gene will be altered if another controlling the same character is introduced. The truth of this statement is evident in ordinary factor interaction, but it is obvious that it must have a wider application in view of the multiple effect of single genes. For the number of factors in any given species must be very great and if, as the evidence indicates, each controls several characters, and influences the general physiology of the organism, the whole body must be bound together by an interacting system. The influence of any one factor on the whole may be slight, but all must combine to form a *gene-complex* providing an internal inherited environment varying from individual to individual. In such an environment, then, every gene has to act. As it is variable, it is evident that the *effect* of a given gene may be changed, even in a constant external environment, but not the gene itself.

This principle is responsible for a phenomenon very common in genetic work, that of the improvement in viability of a new mutation after several generations of inbreeding. Those individuals having a gene-complex with which the gene in question reacts in a particularly disadvantageous way are removed by selection. Of a similar nature are such instances as that worked out by Timoféeff-Ressovsky (1927b) on 'radius incompletus' in *Drosophila funebris*. This character is due to a single factor ; yet it was possible to establish true-breeding stocks in each of which its expression differed, owing to its reaction with a selected gene-complex.

The integrative action of genetic factors may, however, be demonstrated more clearly by the behaviour of such a gene as that producing the 'eyeless' character in *Drosophila melanogaster*. This is a recessive carried in the fourth chromosomes. Its effects are variable, but the eyes are considerably smaller than normal and they may be absent. By selection it has been possible to produce a stock in which most of the flies are without eyes. If, however, an unselected stock, homozygous for the eyeless factor, be inbred for several generations, practically all develop normal eyes. Further inbreeding shows that the modification which has been produced is permanent, and is not the result of temporary changes in the external environment.

This remarkable result is susceptible of two explanations. Either the eyeless factor itself has changed, or the response of the animal to the eyeless factor has changed. It is easy to decide which of these is correct.

If the now highly inbred stock be outcrossed to ordinary wild-type flies, it is found that the extracted recessives which appear in the F2 generation have returned to the original condition. A high proportion of them show the eyeless character in an extreme degree. Thus it is evident that the gene itself must have remained unaltered, for it is capable of exercising its former effects when restored to the original internal environment as supplied by the wild-type flies.

It is clear, then, what has taken place. Among the thousands of genes possessed by the original stock, some would be heterozygous. Recombinations would therefore be possible among them, giving an internal environment differing somewhat in the various individuals. And it is to be noticed that inbreeding, such as that to which the flies were subjected, tends to produce the homozygous condition and so brings hidden recessives into operation. The eyeless gene is thus placed in a number of internal environments, with which it would react in varying degree. But the population competes for food, and in other ways, in the stock bottles. Selection would thus occur, tending to preserve those flies whose gene-complex brings out to the smallest extent the undesirable effects of the eyeless factor ; for this is responsible also for a lowering of vitality and a marked reduction in the number of eggs laid. These effects would in this way gradually be diminished, and flies with practically normal eyes would appear in increasing numbers.

But it is expressly to be noticed that the internal environment is inherited. The stock would be purged by selection of those factors which bring out the maximum effect of the eyeless gene. As long as the inbreeding is maintained, the phenotypic modification would thus persist. On outbreeding, the normal gene-complex would in part be restored, carrying with it factors which intensify the action of the eyeless gene. Thus the original eyeless condition is recovered when the flies homozygous for this gene segregate out as extracted recessives in the second hybrid generation. The range of variation among them is, however, somewhat increased, owing to the segregation of other factors as well as of the eyeless gene itself.

This example shows very clearly how the gene-complex provides an internal environment controlling the effects of individual factors.

3. SUMMARY

Genetic factors interact with the environment to produce the characters for which they are responsible. But the environment is both external and internal. The external environment represents the total effect of the conditions in which the animal lives ; the internal environment is due to the interaction of the whole gene-complex. Alter either the external environment or the gene-complex and the effect of a given factor may be changed. That factors on the whole tend to have characteristic effects is due to the circumstance that every animal has an optimum environment. This it endeavours to maintain as closely as possible, so that the conditions in which factors operate are generally fairly constant.

We have, therefore, no knowledge of the effect of

individual factors. All that can be said is that a given factor will evoke certain characters in a particular external environment and in the presence of all the other factors of the organism.

CHAPTER III

EXPERIMENTAL GENETICS AND ITS BEARING ON EVOLUTION

ANY attempt to apply the results of experimental genetics to the study of evolution has generally provoked a storm of criticism. Among numerous theories of inheritance, Mendelism alone stands out as susceptible of proof and of exact study. Its operation has been demonstrated in the most diverse groups of living organisms, and there are in reality considerations which point rather strongly to the conclusion that it is responsible for the bulk of hereditary variation. Yet it is to the application of this theory that so much exception is taken. It is a matter of great importance, then, to examine why the value of so imposing a body of facts as that presented by the Mendelian phenomena should seriously be called in question when applied to the solution of evolutionary problems.

It must at once be obvious to anyone who has given the matter attention that the characters studied by geneticists do in fact differ fundamentally from those which appear to be responsible for evolutionary progress in nature. It will be valuable to consider this criticism in detail and to determine in how far it is justified.

1. THE PHENOTYPIC EFFECTS OF MUTATION

It may be said that all genetic factors which have arisen by mutation in the laboratory have certain

43

peculiarities in common. It seems that they are nearly always associated with some lowering of vitality as compared with the wild-type form, and the more marked their effect the more deleterious seems to be their action. They appear to be concerned with the production of small superficial differences or with obviously pathological departures from normality which could not in any event survive in a state of nature. Further, nearly all are recessives. A few so-called dominant mutations have certainly occurred · in *Drosophila* and other forms, but these do not in the least represent the production of normal dominant characters such as the wild-type allelomorphs of the recessive mutations. For such genes, though exercising an effect in the heterozygous condition, are not completely dominant and are usually found to be extremely lethal as homozygotes. Indeed, in the majority of such instances the homozygous type is wholly inviable.

There is, then, a sharp distinction between the normal dominant factors found in nature and the recessive genes which arise in the laboratory, a distinction which is emphasized rather than obliterated by occasional dominant mutations, for these generally seem to produce characters of an exceedingly lethal description. It may, in short, be stated that no mutation has ever occurred in the progress of genetic work which is fully viable and behaves as a dominant to the wild-type condition. That any have given rise to changes which could be of survival value in nature appears highly doubtful. It is just possible that in one or two instances they might be of advantage in special circumstances, but this is at any rate quite exceptional. It may legitimately be inquired, therefore, whether the results of genetic research based upon the behaviour of such

genes as these can be applied to the study of evolution
in nature.

It is, of course, to be noticed that many instances
in which variation is controlled in a Mendelian manner
have been detected in animals and plants both in natural
and domesticated conditions. But it must be remem-
bered that the mutations which occur in the laboratory
have provided the material on which most of the
important experimental work has been based, and that
these are nearly always deleterious and generally recessive. There are, however, two considerations which
place this fact in a new light and indicate that the
study of experimental genetics has, after all, a direct
bearing upon the problems of evolution. Firstly, it
can be shown that disadvantageous mutations must in
all circumstances be much more frequent than those
of a favourable kind ; secondly, that a tendency seems
to exist for all disadvantageous mutations gradually
to *become* recessive, while those which confer any
benefit on the organism will progress in the direction
of increasing dominance until they are incorporated in
the normal gene-complex, the former wild-type genes
being converted into recessive allelomorphs.

These points must be examined more minutely. It
is to be observed that mutation is not directional.
There is no evidence that any particular circumstances
cause certain genes to mutate, nor does the quality
of a genic change at a particular locus appear to
be anything but purely fortuitous. On the other
hand, it has already been shown that the genes are
intimately related in function, inasmuch as they form
an interacting gene-complex whose results in a given
environment have been selected as beneficial to the
species. The chances, then, are small that any random
change in this balanced system should fit in with the

delicately adjusted machinery of the gene-complex so as to produce harmonious working. Considered in this light, mutation would be expected most often merely to upset the normal balance of development and produce a lethal effect. Even if it happened so to fit in with the arrangement of existing genes as not to imperil the operation of the whole, the chances are probably extremely remote that the effect thus produced would be of advantage to the organism.

Quite evidently, the more pronounced the changes involved by a particular mutation, the greater are the chances that it will produce an undue disturbance in the existing system. If this is already a very complex one, such a disturbance is even more likely than if it is of a simpler kind. We may therefore anticipate that beneficial mutations will most often involve changes of small magnitude and that they may perhaps be less frequent in highly adapted than in unspecialized organisms.

Some of these considerations have recently been subjected to an exact analysis by Dr. R. A. Fisher. He has demonstrated the low mutation-rates of beneficial mutations in an argument of much interest, based on the chance of survival of a single gene. For further information on this point reference should be made to this study (Fisher, 1930b, pp. 70–83).

It will thus be seen that advantageous mutations are in all circumstances probably very rare indeed. On general grounds they might be expected to occur perhaps once in 10^9 individuals. At any rate, their frequency may be something of this order. Nearly all genic changes therefore will be of a disadvantageous kind, and it is necessary to discuss in what way the organism will react to them.

The possibility that dominance is arrived at by

selection operating on the gene-complex has recently been developed with much success by Dr. Fisher (1928 *a* and *b*, 1929). Briefly this theory may be outlined as follows.

It is known that mutation is a recurrent phenomenon. In *Drosophila* mutations at the white-eye locus have certainly occurred spontaneously more than thirty times and similar, though generally less frequent, repetitions have been observed at other loci, and in various species both of animals and plants. It is not known what relation the mutation rate in nature bears to that under experimental conditions, though mutations such as those observed in the laboratory certainly occur naturally. For instance, the first gene to be discovered in *Drosophila simulans* was that for yellow body-colour. It is a sex-linked recessive, and was found by Metz in a wild specimen obtained in Florida (Sturtevant, 1921*b*, p. 44). It has been proved to be identical with the gene for yellow body-colour in *Drosophila melanogaster* (*ibid.*, p. 47). Gershenson (1928) detected a sex-linked, and sex-controlled, factor in *Drosophila obscura* in natural conditions. Its effects are confined to the male and are purely lethal, since it prevents the formation of nearly all spermatozoa bearing the Y-chromosome and gives rise to a sex-ratio of about 96 females : 4 males. Such genes as these are of a type quite similar to the disadvantageous recessives which arise by mutation in the laboratory. More recently, the studies of Dubinin and his collaborators (1934) on *Drosophila melanogaster*, and of Dobzhansky and Queal (1938) on *D. pseudo-obscura*, have demonstrated that recessive genes in the heterozygous state are widely spread in wild populations of these species. Similar evidence is also accumulating for other organisms.

There can be no doubt that in every species the

total number of individuals breeding in a single year
must greatly exceed the total number ever subjected
to genetic analysis ; this must even be true for *Drosophila melanogaster* of which, astonishing as it may
seem, many millions have been bred and examined
under experimental conditions. We may feel confident,
then, that few if any of the mutations which have
occurred in the course of genetic work are in reality
novelties. The species must already have had a long
experience of them and have been able to adjust itself
to them, if in fact any such adjustment is possible.
The strong probability that it is will be apparent in
view of the interaction of the genes with the internal
environment which has already been outlined.

It is normally to be expected that two doses of a
gene should be more efficacious than one, so that when
a mutation occurs for the first time in the history of
a species we may fairly assume that the resulting heterozygote will have an effect intermediate between that
produced by either homozygote ; of this there is some
evidence, as will shortly appear. So long as a gene
is rare in the population it will occur vastly more often
in the heterozygous than in the homozygous state.
For in such circumstances the chances of two heterozygotes mating will be remote ; far more often a
heterozygote will mate with an ordinary wild-type
individual, and the new gene will be passed on to
half the offspring, once more as a heterozygote. Clearly,
then, the reaction of a species to any really new mutation
will be adjusted to the effect which the resultant gene
produces in the heterozygous state.

Now the gene-complex is not constant even in nature.
It varies owing to a certain amount of heterozygosity,
which allows recombinations of factors to take place.
A new gene will thus be placed in a number of different

internal environments, with which it will react to a varying degree. Should its effects be of a disadvantageous
kind, selection will favour those combinations of factors
which bring them out to the smallest extent. There
will thus be a constant tendency operating to modify
the reaction of the species in such a way that the effects
of a disadvantageous gene will be masked in the heterozygote, so leading to recessiveness. This process is,
in fact, quite comparable to that already described in
such instances as the eyeless character, in which the
disadvantageous phenotype was proved to be obliterated by selection of factors forming the internal environment. The only difference is that we were then dealing
with the production of recessiveness in the homozygous
instead of in the heterozygous condition.

Ultimately, when the recessive state has been
attained, a similar but even slower process favouring
the obliteration of the disadvantageous effects of the
homozygote might be expected to take place. This
should end in the gene ceasing to have any effects at
all in normal circumstances. If, however, another
mutation controlling similar characters were to arise,
such an old and ineffective gene might show itself as
a 'specific modifier'. Consider, for instance, an allelomorphic pair controlling the rate at which pigment is
produced in the body, such as the factors for the production of black and red facets in the eyes of *Gammarus*.
If the wild-type allelomorph (the dominant black factor)
of such a pair produces pigment up to saturation value
very quickly, any small effect left to a similar mutation,
which had been subjected to long-continued counter-
selection, would be undetectable. Such a gene might,
however, still have the opportunity of exerting some
effect if pigment production were greatly delayed by
some other factor, such as that producing the red eye.

For the facets then remain for a long time in a sensitive condition in which it is possible to observe very small changes in the rate of melanin production. In this way certain factors might come to have an effect only in the presence of a particular gene. These have already been mentioned in Chapter II, and their presence has also been demonstrated in the instance discussed here. For it has been shown (Ford and Huxley, 1927, pp. 115–23) that there exist more than one pair of factors affecting, to a very slight degree, the rate of melanin deposition in the eyes of *Gammarus*. This they do in a manner quite similar to that of the pair responsible for the major control of this process. Their effect, however, is so minute that they can only be demonstrated in the slowly darkening red-eyed condition, produced by the retardation of melanin development. The origin of such ' specific modifiers ' has long been a matter for speculation, as the occurrence of genes solely concerned in modifying others, which are themselves evidently incapable of becoming established in nature, has seemed difficult to explain. It appears, however, that they may be the result of long-continued counter-selection acting on a disadvantageous mutation in the manner here outlined.

In the rare event of a beneficial mutation, a process the reverse of that so far described would take place. The gene-complex which brings out the effects of the heterozygote to the greatest extent would be selected, and the new mutant gene would become dominant to the original wild-type allelomorph, which it would automatically supplant.

The effects of the more markedly lethal genes must, on the other hand, be uninfluenced by selection. The individuals carrying them will be at such a disadvantage that they will generally be killed off whenever they appear, and there will be no opportunity for selection of the gene-complex to take place in respect to them. To this class, no doubt, belong the rare semi-dominant and highly inviable mutations which occur from time to time in genetic work. They will have left too few descendants to have modified much the reaction of the species to them, even as heterozygotes.

Thus it is not to be expected that completely domin-ant genes having new and advantageous effects should appear as mutations in genetic experiments. Complete dominance is probably the result of selection accentu-ating the effects of an initially beneficial heterozygote, and a gene of this kind should be quickly incorporated in the wild-type constitution. The production of dominance in a new favourable mutation should be a far more rapid process than the corresponding drift towards recessiveness in a disadvantageous gene, which is continually being extinguished by counter-selection ; for this can only be brought about by recurrent muta-tion.

It will be seen that on the theory here outlined dominance is to be regarded as one of the phenotypic effects of a gene. It is to be expected, therefore, that it will be susceptible to such modifications as affect the other manifestations of genic action. We may now discuss a few of the facts which support this point of view.

Consider first the action of the external environ-ment. It is perhaps hardly to be expected that once the completely recessive condition has been established, external changes within the toleration of the species should be capable of restoring marked phenotypic activity to the heterozygote. For the fact that counter-selection may continue to act upon the homozygote will always tend to reduce the effects of disadvantageous

genes beyond what may, in normal circumstances, be
the bare minimum necessary to inhibit them in the
heterozygous state. Small variations produced by
changes in the external environment would probably
therefore not be detectable, though they might be
where the production of complete recessiveness has not
been attained. Instances of this kind have, in fact,
been observed. For example, the bar-eye factor in
Drosophila melanogaster, which is an incomplete dominant, reduces the number of facets in the eyes and its
effect can be expressed quantitatively. Hersh (1924,
1927) found that the degree of dominance of this character varies with the temperature at which the flies are
bred.

The chief interest, however, attaches to the
modification of dominance due to changes in the
internal environment. The important general effects
which such changes produce upon the action of genes
have already been discussed in Chapter II. It will
therefore be necessary only to mention here certain
instances which throw special light upon the origin of
dominance.

Dr. Fisher (*l.c.*) has already drawn attention to the
interesting behaviour of the ' crinkled-dwarf ' factor
which arose as a mutation in Sea Island cotton. In
this species it is a simple recessive, while in the other
New World cottons it has not been observed. It can,
however, be introduced into them by crossing. This
has been done by Dr. S. C. Harland, who finds that
crinkled-dwarf is no longer a recessive in the F1 plants,
while in F2 every degree of dominance seems to appear,
giving apparently continuous variation. It is evident,
therefore, that the gene-complex of the Sea Island
cotton is so adjusted as to inhibit the effects of the
crinkled-dwarf factor in the heterozygous state, while

no such adjustment has taken place in the species unaccustomed to this mutation.

Somewhat similar evidence may be obtained from a
consideration of the various effects of a single gene.
Dobzhansky (1927, p. 383) has shown that the allelomorphic factors at the white-eye locus, and the wild-
type, sooty, and ebony body-colour series in *Drosophila*,
have a secondary effect on the shape of the spermatheca.
They produce small but exceedingly constant changes
in proportion which are practically uninfluenced by
external conditions, which, however, alter the absolute
size of this organ very considerably. It is difficult to
see that such changes as these can be controlled by
direct selection. On the other hand, body-colour, or
eye colour in so far as it can influence the efficiency of
vision, must be of direct importance in the insects.
It is therefore a striking fact that while the genes controlling these characters are completely recessive in so
far as their external effects are concerned, yet in the
shape of the spermatheca the heterozygotes are intermediate. It would appear that selection has been
able to produce the recessive condition in respect of
disadvantageous characters, without influencing their
harmless secondary effects.

It has been suggested, then, that selection of the
gene-complex in respect of particular factors may take
place in two ways; first, by favouring the action of one
rather than the other allelomorph in the heterozygote,
and later by the obliteration of the effects of a gene
even in the homozygous condition. It will be a crucial
test, therefore, to examine the reaction of factors when
balanced against each other in combinations such as
cannot previously have occurred, or have at any rate
been of such excessive rarity as to have left no im-
pression upon the species. It is evident that such

combinations as these can be provided by the multiple allelomorphs.

A number of different changes at the same locus may each occur as mutations. These will of course be very rare, and each will therefore find itself in competition with the wild-type allelomorph, since, as previously pointed out, in rare genes the heterozygote is immensely commoner than the homozygote in wild populations. As such genes will nearly always be disadvantageous they will be prevented from spreading widely. It is evident, therefore, that the chances are almost infinitely remote that two different mutant members of the same series of allelomorphs can find themselves in competition with each other in natural conditions. Now the re-actions of multiple allelomorphs are well known in a number of forms. It has been found that though in general each behaves as a simple recessive to the wild-type gene, when the two members of such a series are brought together by experimental crossing, the hetero-zygote so formed is intermediate between them. This relationship seems to exist in all the instances studied ; it occurs in the most diverse forms, for example in *Drosophila* (Morgan, Bridges, and Sturtevant, 1925, pp. 34–6) and Rodents (Feldman, 1924). It is plain that this provides a very important corroboration of the theories discussed in this chapter, for it shows that a condition of dominance and recessiveness has been established between such factors as can normally have been in competition, but not between two factors which probably have never been brought together before.

Certain objections can be raised to the efficiency of such selection as is here described. Of these the most important is the contention that it is not sufficiently powerful to produce an effect except in artificial con-ditions, owing to the rarity of heterozygotes in nature.

This view has been supported on mathematical
grounds by Sewall Wright (1929 *a* and *b*). Fisher's
calculations (Fisher, 1929), published in answer to
those of Sewall Wright, would seem to indicate,
however, that it must be a factor of importance. It
has indeed now been possible to produce dominance-
modification experimentally in a wild species, the Cur-
rant Moth *Abraxas grossulariata*. The variety *lutea*,
which converts the ground-colour from the normal
white to yellow, has an intermediate effect in the
heterozygous state. By selection of the more and of
the less extreme heterozygotes respectively, it has been
possible to make this variety almost a dominant in one
line and almost a recessive in another (Ford, 1940).

It may further be doubted whether the gene-complex
is capable of modification in many directions at once,
as is required for the adjustment of the numerous
mutations which occur from time to time. But, in
the majority of instances the alteration in the phenotypic effects of a gene will probably be brought about
principally by selection operating on comparatively
few factors ; generally those which are concerned in
controlling the same characters, or at any rate the
same developmental effects, as the gene in question.

An interesting alternative suggestion of the manner
in which dominance may be attained has been made
by J. B. S. Haldane (1930). He draws attention
to the strong probability that many genes may act up
to a saturation value beyond which no effect can be
obtained. Now it is clear that any mutations occurring
in a gene which has reached saturation level can only
be detected if they take place in a minus direction and,
in consequence, a number of phenotypically inseparable
mutations of higher value might become available for
recombination. Haldane suggests that those hetero-

zygotes will be selected in which loss mutations are balanced by allelomorphs so much above saturation level that the combined action of the pair is not reduced below it. Thus there would be no reduction in activity in the heterozygous condition, and dominance would result.

It will be seen that on this view dominance is also brought about by selection, but that this is assumed to operate on multiple allelomorphs rather than on the gene-complex. Now there is good reason for supposing that in many instances the genes do in fact act up to a saturation value. In wild-type *Gammarus* the factor controlling melanin deposition is certainly responsible for the production of more pigment than is necessary to make the facets black. As already pointed out (p. 30), a recessive gene inducing melanin formation in relatively small quantities can produce complete blackening before the facets have increased in size. In larger eyes, however, the amount of melanin may not be sufficient wholly to obscure the red pigment. It is evident, then, that in some environments reduction in the activity of the melanin-producing factor in *Gammarus* could take place without producing detectable effects. The same conclusion is arrived at by the important work of Stern (1929), who was able to build up the normal dominant condition in *Drosophila* by accumulating the recessive multiple allelomorphs of the character ' bobbed ' (*bb*) carried in extra Y-chromosomes. It is apparent, then, that the amount of genic material present at a locus can have a quantitative effect and, where this acts up to a saturation value beyond which the phenotype cannot be altered, complete dominance will result, provided that this value is exceeded in the heterozygote.

It has, however, been pointed out (Ford, 1930) that

such saturation levels cannot be regarded as fixtures inherent in the species, but they must be determined by the activity of the organism as a whole. They must therefore respond to changes in the gene-complex, so that selection of the type postulated by Fisher may none the less be the primary factor controlling dominance even where selection of particular multiple allelomorphs takes place in the manner suggested by Haldane.

Although, as we have seen, the occurrence of new mutations immediately ousting the wild type is not to be anticipated, reverse mutations from a recessive gene back to the normal allelomorph have been known to take place. This would be expected if the wild-type characters were originally due to such mutations as occur in experimental work, but not if these latter are an abnormal phenomenon playing no part in the evolution of species in natural conditions.

All instances of apparent reverse mutation must be critically examined, as it cannot always be proved that the appearance of a normal individual in a stock homozygous for some recessive gene is not due to the accidental introduction of a wild-type specimen. In certain instances, however, this possibility can be excluded. Thus Timoféeff-Ressovsky (1927a), working on ' radius incompletus ' in *Drosophila funebris*, discovered a normal fly in a homozygous stock after twenty-four generations of inbreeding ; on testing it was found to be heterozygous, and consequently could not have been accidentally introduced. The radius incompletus factor is not always phenotypically expressed ; but such apparent returns to normality had often been tested, and on all previous occasions had proved to be genotypically pure. Shisan Chen (1928) obtained an autosomal mutation producing ' transparency ' in the course of his studies on gold-fish. He also obtained somatic mutation of the normal to the transparent gene and the reverse. Other instances might be cited. One which illustrates an important genetic situation is the mutation of the gene for miniature wings in *Drosophila virilis* studied by Demereč (1926, 1929 *a* and *b*). This often reverts to the wild-type allelomorph, and the frequency and type of mutation, whether germinal or somatic, is partly controlled by other genes.

Of special interest is the fact that reverse mutation from a recessive gene back to the normal allelomorph has been produced by X-rays (see, for example, Timoféeff-Ressovsky, 1929, and Patterson, 1929). For it has been maintained that the induction of mutation by this means is to be regarded as proof that recessive genes are abnormalities, since they can arise when, as it is suggested, damage has been done to the germ plasm by a source of destructive nature. Such a conclusion is seen to be untenable. If some mutations represent damage to the chromosomes, others represent the repair of this damage ; the agent which in one case produces the wound is the same which heals it in the other !

2. DOMESTICATION

As so many genetic problems have been studied on domestic animals and plants, it will at this point be convenient briefly to consider the effects which the peculiar conditions to which they are subject have on the phenotypic expression of their genes. Not only are domesticated species protected from rigorous selection, but types actually disadvantageous in natural conditions may be favoured by man, either for special purposes or merely as curiosities. For this reason many of the genetic factors found in domestic species differ considerably in their behaviour from those so far described.

It has been pointed out that in *Drosophila*, and other forms used in laboratory experiments, mutations give rise either to recessive genes or to imperfect dominants, usually of a very lethal description. Yet in domesticated species it is quite common to find healthy varieties produced by genes whose effect is detectable in the heterozygote. Such viable imperfect dominants or recessives are known in cattle, sheep, horses, dogs, cats, rabbits, guinea-pigs and other forms. It is often extremely doubtful, however, if such varieties could survive in natural conditions. We may suspect that the genes which are now responsible for them have been arising by recurrent mutation in the past, and that they were constantly being eliminated by selection, leading to complete dominance of the wild-type form.

Such recessive mutations would be seized upon as novelties during domestication and preserved. Those individuals in which their effects were most apparent would be used for breeding, and the type accentuated by a selection of the gene-complex the reverse of that which had proceeded in nature. In this way many of the mutations might be brought back to a state in which the heterozygote is affected. Such artificial selection would of course be extremely rapid compared with the corresponding process in nature.

Once a distinct difference had appeared, the heterozygous form, rather than either homozygote, seems to have been especially valued in certain instances ; as perhaps the red-roan coat colour in Shorthorn cattle, and certainly the ' blue ' plumage in Andalusian fowls. Here the change would be even more speedy and profound, for no attempt would be made to select the gene-complex in such a way that either homozygote should approach the desired form. The most valued individuals would naturally be bred from, so that direct selection would take place for those heterozygotes which differ most from either homozygous type.

Finally, it may be mentioned that in poultry a quite exceptional condition is found, for some of the factors which separate the domestic breeds from the wild jungle-fowl are actually complete dominants. The dominant white plumage of the White Leghorn, and the rose and pea combs, are familiar examples. This evidently presents a somewhat different problem from that already discussed. A satisfactory explanation of it has, in the opinion of the writer, been arrived at by Dr. Fisher (1928 *b*). He points out that the original conditions of domestication of the poultry, which took place in Burma, differed from those of most animals ; for there the flocks were, and often still are, subject to constant crossing from wild individuals. In this way the normal allelomorphs of any mutations were continually being brought in, so that selection could only proceed in favour of such genes as initially showed at least some slight effect in the heterozygote. This conclusion has now been verified by Fisher (1935, 1938). He reversed the presumed evolutionary process by introducing genes dominant in domestic poultry into the wild jungle-fowl : these then exercised distinct heterozygous effects.

As soon as domestic poultry had been spread by human agency beyond the natural range of their wild representative, these peculiar conditions would no longer prevail. Recurrent mutations which had become recessive through natural selection would then stand a fair chance of being detected when they occurred in the flocks. We therefore find that numerous varieties dependent upon recessive as well as dominant factors have been established in domestic poultry.

3. SUMMARY AND CONCLUSIONS

Mutations occurring in the laboratory give rise either to recessive genes or to semi-dominants, generally of a definitely lethal description. Either type is, however, nearly always associated with at least some decrease in viability, nor do such mutations produce changes which are likely to be of advantage in nature. It appears, however, that disadvantageous mutations must be immensely more common than those conferring any benefit on the organism, and that a tendency exists for them gradually to *become* recessive. This is due to recurrent mutation enabling selection of the gene-complex to take place in favour of those heterozygotes which have the least marked effect. A continuation of such selection acting on the homozygote will lead to the obliteration of the phenotypic effects of a gene, except in certain circumstances in which it might act as a specific modifier. If a mutation is initially very lethal no change can, however, occur, and the gene remains as a more or less inviable semi-dominant.

In the rare advantageous mutations a process the reverse of that so far described will take place ; the new gene will rapidly become dominant and be incorporated in the wild-type gene-complex.

The peculiar conditions to which domestic animals are subjected lead to a mitigation or reversal of selection. This accounts for the fact that genes producing characters of normal viability, with effects detectable in the heterozygote, may be found among them. In certain instances, seemingly amenable to special explanation, the heterozygote may differ considerably from either homozygote, or varieties may actually be established which behave as complete dominants to the wild-type form.

It will be seen therefore that the fact that laboratory

mutations generally give rise to recessive genes, of a kind unlikely to establish themselves in nature, does not mean that they represent a condition fundamentally different from the production of their wild-type allelomorphs. The results of genetic research can therefore legitimately be used in the interpretation of natural phenomena.

CHAPTER IV

THE APPLICATION OF THE MENDELIAN THEORY TO EVOLUTIONARY PROBLEMS IN NATURE

1. MENDELISM AS THE BASIS OF ORGANIC INHERITANCE

THE considerations brought forward in the last chapter indicate that the results of experimental genetics are directly applicable to the study of evolutionary problems in nature. It was seen that though the wild-type factors differ so markedly from their recessive allelomorphs, yet both may have been arrived at by similar processes of mutation and selection. Before any further use can be made of this important conclusion, it must be inquired whether we are justified in supposing all inheritance to be of the Mendelian type.

Two supplementary methods of inheritance can be suggested in opposition to this view. First, that the most fundamental part of inheritance is, in fact, maternal; it may be that the main outlines of each organism are dependent upon qualities inherent in the cytoplasm, while only the more superficial characters are controlled by the activity of the nucleus, and are in consequence supplied equally by both parents. Secondly that, in so far as inheritance is bi-parental, there may be behind the Mendelian phenomena an elusive background of blending inheritance too subtle so far to have been subjected to experimental study. These two possibilities must now briefly be considered.

The first, that inheritance may not be wholly bi-sexual, certainly presents the more difficult problem. It has recently been revived by Russell (1930), and very possibly it may contain some measure of truth. But the substantial equality between each parent and the offspring in biometrical correlations seems to exclude uni-sexual, and therefore cytoplasmic, inheritance as a phenomenon of wide application, except for those basic characters whose variation cannot be studied, and to these we shall return.

Purely maternal (Non-Mendelian) inheritance is, of course, known to occur, as, for example, the plastid inheritance which may be responsible for certain kinds of albinism in plants. Thus Correns (1909) studied a race of the Common Four-o'clock (*Mirabilis jalapa*) in which the leaves are made up of patches of green and white, while entire branches may sometimes be of one or the other colour. He showed that self-fertilized flowers on a green branch produce permanently true-breeding green plants, those on a white branch only white, while those on checkered branches give white, green, and checkered offspring in proportions relative to the amount of green and white on the branch from which the flower comes. Crosses between flowers on green and white branches give offspring which inherit the colour of the maternal branch only, whichever way the cross is made. It may, in parenthesis, be noticed that the control of chlorophyll production may also be directly Mendelian, as instanced by the work of Collins already mentioned (p. 32).

Such rare cytoplasmic inheritance as this does not, however, touch the fundamental problem with which we are concerned. The question remains to be settled whether or not the characters determining the basic development of the species, according to the phylum, class, or order to which it belongs, are bi-sexually inherited. Perhaps the only definite evidence which can throw any light on this important question is to be obtained from the work on experimentally produced larval hybrids. Boveri (1903) was able to fertilize enucleated eggs of *Sphærechinus* with the sperm of *Echinus*. He found that the skeleton of the resulting larva was purely paternal in type, so that the sperm nucleus was capable of controlling the generic characters of the skeleton in a cross between these two closely related Echinoids. Godlewski (1906), on the other hand, succeeded in fertilizing enucleated eggs of the Echinoid *Echinus* with sperm of the Crinoid *Antedon*. All the offspring died at an early stage, but in a few, development proceeded sufficiently far for gastrulæ to be formed. In these it was apparent that the cleavage and mode of gastrulation was purely maternal. The sperm nucleus, therefore, though supplying the only nuclear material present, was unable to impose upon the foreign cytoplasm a course of development typical of another Class.

We see, then, that such fundamental characters as skeletal differences are controlled wholly by the nucleus in a cross between two nearly related species. The most important matter, however, is to decide what interpretation can be placed upon the result of the wider cross. Since Godlewski made no measurements of nuclear size, it has been suggested by Boveri that these supposedly haploid gastrulæ came from fragments in which the nuclei were present but were invisible in the living state and, consequently, that they represented a condition of parthenogenesis through activation by the foreign sperm. If, however, the experiment can be accepted in its full force, it certainly indicates that, in this instance at least, the cytoplasm of the egg is alone concerned in determining the type of cleavage. But the cytoplasm develops in the presence of the maternal nucleus and gene-complex, and this may be responsible for directing the early development, perhaps before the new diploid nucleus can exercise its effect.

The strong probability of this is indicated by the work of Tennent in fertilizing the normal (nucleated) eggs of *Cidaris* with the sperm of *Lytechinus* (Morgan, 1927, p. 635). In the latter genus development proceeds much more rapidly than in the former, and the origin of the mesenchyme cells is different. In the cross-fertilized egg no effect of the sperm is observable before gastrulation begins, for the rate of cleavage is not hastened and the blastula has the appearance typical of *Cidaris*. The origin of the mesenchyme, however, is intermediate between the two parental types. In the hybrids it is not formed until after gastrulation has begun, and by that time the cytoplasmic-nuclear relation has been restored to normal. Godlewski (1925) has shown that in the Echinoderms this is usually about $7 : 1$. In the mature egg it is $400 : 1$, in the four-cell stage of the embryo $18 : 1$, in the sixty-one-cell stage $12 : 1$, while in the fully-formed blastula it has returned to its normal value.

It may well be, therefore, that the nucleus is unable to control a volume of cytoplasm relatively so great as that found in the earliest stages of development, but that it asserts its effect when the normal conditions are restored. The course of development up to that time may be determined by the maternal gene-complex. We have no clear evidence that this is so, but such an assumption is quite a legitimate one in view of the fact that instances are actually known in which the parental gene-complex imposes an effect upon the next generation as, for example, the important researches of Diver (1925) on *Limnœa* have clearly shown.

It is thus apparent that, contrary to what might at first be suspected, the experiments of Godlewski are quite incapable of deciding the question whether or not the early stages of development are determined by purely cytoplasmic or by nuclear inheritance. The early development of the two genera of Echinoids used by Boveri is identical, no difference between them could in any event be detected until the formation of the skeleton. To this stage the offspring of Godlewski's inter-Class cross never attained ; no evidence therefore is available to show whether or not the Crinoid nucleus could affect the Echinoid egg in the later stages. Thus the two experiments are in no sense contradictory.

It appears then that, in so far as the evidence goes, the most fundamental characters are determined by the nucleus, that is bi-sexually, except perhaps those which are responsible for the main outline of development characteristic of the phylum, class, or order to which the species belongs. Even in this matter the evidence we possess is consistent with the view, established on general grounds, that such characters are in reality controlled by nuclear action.

It remains, therefore, to be considered whether all nuclear inheritance is Mendelian. It is a significant fact that though many instances are known in which crossing results in continuous variation in the F2 generation, rather than sharp segregation, yet detailed study has always indicated that the blending so produced is apparent rather than real. The interaction of several factors having cumulative effects may make it impossible to separate the phenotypes at segregation. Other complications lead to a similar condition ; for example, the heterozygote may overlap both homozygotes to a greater or lesser extent. But the particulate nature of such inheritance is demonstrated by the greater range of variation in the F2 than in the F1 generation, for this is not to be anticipated if blending were to occur. It is further supported by the fact that the more extreme forms which are recovered show at least a considerable return to one or other of the grand-parental types. The proportion in which these types themselves segregate out of a cross is, of course, extremely small if several factors are involved, and very great numbers of F2 individuals would have to be bred in order to obtain them.

Although it appears that the facts of heredity as established by experiment cannot be explained on the assumption of blending inheritance, it is obvious that this does not by any means exclude the possibility that such occurs. It may be argued that the characters controlled by this means are not of a kind which can be studied by the experimental methods so far employed. Indeed, the position of those who support such a theory appears at first sight to be a safe one ; as new facts come to light, extending more and more widely the application of Mendelism, they can always retract their claims, maintaining that only characters of the most fundamental kind are subject to blending. It has, however, been pointed out by R. A. Fisher (1930b, p. 18) in an argument of much ingenuity that, in certain instances at least, the possibility of blending inheritance can be wholly excluded. Only the main outlines of this demonstration will be discussed here, as detailed information on the subject can be obtained from the work in question.

It is evident that one of the most important ways in which particulate inheritance differs from any blending mechanism is in its capacity to maintain the variability of the species. With particulate inheritance the rate at which variation is extinguished is, in large populations, exceedingly slow ; with blending inheritance it is halved at each generation in matings between unrelated individuals, while even quite close inbreeding serves only to retard this process to a slight extent.

With blending inheritance, therefore, either uniformity must quickly be reached or else the variability must constantly be maintained by mutation. Now there can be no doubt that much inherited variation occurs among wild species, and it is certainly found abundantly among those subject to domestication. Yet, as pointed out previously, mutation is a rare phenomenon ; its frequency appears to be of the order necessary to maintain variability when conserved by particulate inheritance. There can be no doubt at all that it is far too infrequent to provide the constant supply of new variation which would be required if a considerable proportion of the characters were subject to blending.

This consideration serves only to support the conclusion already reached, that Mendelism is responsible for the bulk of organic inheritance. But Dr. Fisher has drawn attention to the fact that the work on ' pure-lines ', when studied from this point of view, supplies more definite information. Self-fertilization rapidly leads to a condition of homozygosity, since all factors already homozygous must remain so, while the number of heterozygous allelomorphs is rapidly reduced, half becoming homozygous at each generation. Johannsen (1903, 1913), working on a species of bean, was able to establish a number of such homozygous lines, in which hereditary variation is of course entirely absent. He showed that within such lines selection for size and other characters is unavailing even when continued for more than ten generations, although the fact that a number of different lines were established proved that heritable

6

variation is normally present in the species. Fisher
(*ibid.*) points out that had any appreciable proportion
of such variation been dependent upon blending inheritance, the stream of mutations necessary to maintain it
would, in ten generations, have supplied it almost to the
maximum degree and must certainly have been revealed
by selection. Only two mutations actually appeared.

2. MENDELISM AND SELECTION

We have now reached two important conclusions ;
that the results of experimental genetics may safely be
applied to the solution of evolutionary problems in
nature, and that the great bulk, and perhaps the whole,
of organic inheritance must be of the Mendelian type.
These enable us to draw certain deductions from the
facts so far considered. We have seen that genetic
factors interact with their internal environment, and
that their effects can in consequence be altered by
selection operating on the gene-complex ; the way in
which this produces the conditions of dominance and
recessiveness has already been discussed. It is evident,
however, that such selection opens up another possibility of considerable importance for evolutionary
theory ; that the effects of a given gene may gradually
alter. We have, in fact, no ground for assuming that
the characters to which a particular gene gives rise are
those which it produced at its first appearance. We
are therefore confronted with two distinct effects of
selection, which have not generally received separate
recognition. First, that an inherited character conferring any advantage on the individual will tend to spread
through the species, since the individuals which possess
it will be favoured by selection ; secondly, that the
effects of a gene, if advantageous, may be intensified,
and perhaps altered in quality, owing to the tendency

for those individuals to be preserved whose gene-complex
brings them out to the greatest extent.

The first of these processes, the natural selection of
characters, is of course familiar to all students of Biology,
and has gained general acceptance. It is not seriously
doubted that individuals possessing any specially advantageous character will on the whole contribute more to
the ancestry of future generations than those which
fall below the average standard of the species and that,
in so far as such departures from the mean are inherited,
this process will lead to evolutionary change. This is
pure Darwinism, and assumes no special type of inheritance. The second, the natural selection of factors,
is one which follows inevitably from such facts as those
discussed in Chapter II (pp. 38–42), and is the outcome of Mendelian research. It will be found to remove
some of the difficulties felt by those who hold that the
principles of particulate inheritance are at variance with
what is known of evolutionary progress.

These difficulties are of several kinds, but they may
perhaps be grouped under three main headings. Two
of these have already been discussed : that the genes
appear to be chiefly responsible for the production of
characters which could not be of value to the organism,
and the possibility that they contribute only a part of
the heritable variation of the species. The third is due
to the idea that the characters controlled by Mendelian
inheritance arise ready-made by mutation, to be selected
or rejected in the struggle for existence as the case may
be. Such a discontinuous origin of characters is, in its
crudest sense, rightly felt to be inconsistent with the
slow and continuous course of evolution. This objec-
tion has been stated clearly by Professor MacBride
(1930), who says that the theory has been espoused by
some writers that evolution proceeds by sudden jumps

or ' mutations ' like the sports which occasionally turn
up in the farmyard or garden, and that occasionally
one of these sports, which occur for no assignable cause,
' chances ' to fit the demands of the environment and
survives. He continues : ' Suffice it to say that this
doctrine . . . finds no countenance with those really
competent to speak on the subject of evolution. Our
leading systematists, palæontologists, and embryologists
are all convinced that evolution has been slow, functional,
and continuous.'

It is to be noticed that this criticism omits all reference to an important condition of the theory : the size
of the mutational steps involved. Clearly if these were
very small, almost continuous evolutionary progress
could result. That many genes which become incorporated in the species have, in fact, arisen by mutations which gave rise to minute changes will be apparent
from a consideration of the discussion in Chapter III
(Section 1), in which it was shown that beneficial mutations will most often involve changes of small magnitude. It is, however, well known that many genes do
produce striking effects, and to these the criticism now
under discussion might at first sight seem to apply. It is,
however, to be noticed that many such genes are successful and have been able to establish themselves in
nature ; among many other forms, the Lepidoptera,
especially those displaying mimetic resemblances, show
numerous clear instances of this. In *Papilio polytes*,
Papilio memnon, and the genus *Hypolimnas*, for example,
polymorphism involving the most striking changes is
certainly controlled by single factors. It may then be
inquired how adaptations such as these have been
brought about.

We would of course agree with Professor MacBride
that it is quite unthinkable that mutation after muta-

tion could have appeared until at last one happened to hit off the wonderful resemblance which we see between mimic and model in these insects, and that this could have happened repeatedly in a great number of species. As pointed out a few years ago by Fisher (1927), the solution is probably to be found in the interaction of individual genes with the gene-complex, in the manner already outlined.

We have no reason to assume that when genes such as these first appeared their effects were similar to those which they produce to-day. On the contrary, we may suppose that in a given palatable species a gene arose which chanced to give some slight resemblance to a protected form. This would gradually be improved by selection of the gene-complex, and the consequent altera-tion of the effects produced by all the genes acting to-gether, until an accurate mimicry had been attained. Such a process would be one of slow continuous change, but at the end the profound difference so produced would still be under the control of a single factor ; yet this would not mean that the mimic had arisen from the non-mimetic form suddenly by a single act of mutation.

It will thus be apparent that though genetic factors have their origin in spontaneous mutation, this does not in the least imply that the characters which they control are not susceptible of slow and continuous evolutionary change.

This is a conclusion of considerable importance. It is, of course, an extension of the theory of dominance which was discussed in the last chapter, and it is evident that an advantageous gene will become completely dominant, in the manner there described, at the same time that its effects are being improved. There is, of course, no need to assume that such a gene possessed any advantage from the outset. Initially disadvantageous and virtually non-adaptive genes may ultimately become established through changes either in the external or the internal environment. A character which is of no advantage at one period in the development of a species may be useful at another, and a factor which is of no value in one gene-complex may have beneficial effects in another, while the recurrent nature of mutation allows the genes to make repeated bids for success.

It is evident that domestication, with its artificial selection, will greatly increase the rate at which genic improvement can take place. It is to be expected that when attention is more generally directed to this matter such changes will be observed in numerous domesticated species. They have, indeed, been detected even at the present time. For example, the fish *Lebistes reticulatus* has for many years been bred in captivity for aquarium purposes. The males are polymorphic, and Winge finds that the various forms supplied by dealers are often more ' beautiful ' than those to be obtained in the wild state, suggesting that appreciable modification has been brought about by human selection (see Fisher, 1930*a*, p. 399). Furthermore, Winge (1927, pp. 34–5) was himself able to show that the effects of one of these genes, that known as *maculatus*, could definitely be altered by selection.

Although in natural conditions such processes as these are most likely to take place over long periods of time, during which considerable changes may be expected in the environment, both external and internal, and in the needs of the organism, it seems possible that special opportunities for genic improvement may sometimes occur. It has been established by Elton (1924, 1925, and 1927, pp. 127–45 ; 1930, pp. 7–35) that fluctuation in numbers is a phenomenon of wide occurrence in animal communities, and that in many instances it is subject to a regular periodicity, giving rise to cycles of abundance and rarity. He has therefore pointed out that the opportunity for the spread of genes which fluctuation provides may be an important factor in evolution. In order to explain the non-adaptive nature of the characters which are sometimes known to separate closely related species, he suggested that this process may lead to non-adaptive evolutionary change. Such an idea must, however, be received with caution.

It is apparent that when a mutation chances to occur in a population which is rapidly increasing, it will be enabled to spread in a way which would be impossible if the numbers had remained constant and each pair had on the average been giving rise to but a single pair in the next generation. Practically non-adaptive or even disadvantageous genes would thus be placed in a number of different gene-complexes, with which they would have the opportunity of reacting in various ways. Should one of these chance to be beneficial, the effect so produced would be favoured by selection. This would lead to the establishment of such a gene, and of the gene-complex with which it reacted usefully. When the increase in numbers ceases, the spread of non-adaptive genes would be checked, and those of a semi-lethal character quickly eradicated ; this process being, of course, even more swift when, as so frequently happens, periodic fluctuations take place, leading on to a decline in the population. Any advantageous combination which had arisen would, however, maintain its footing at this time, and lead to an adaptive change in the population as a whole.

Fluctuation in numbers, then, may give an opportunity for normal evolutionary processes to take place more rapidly. For so long as the numbers remain constant the rate at which a non-adaptive character can spread is so excessively slow as to be almost negligible, while the opportunities for recombination accorded to a disadvantageous gene must be small indeed. With an increasing population, in which each pair is giving rise to a number of mature individuals in the next generation, such genes have a much greater chance of spreading and so varying their characters. It would appear, however, that in general an evolutionary change will only take place if an advantageous variation results from this process. For a gene which remains non-adaptive will on the average only affect the same proportion of the population as at its first appearance, though with a large increase this may represent a considerable number of individuals. When the population is again reduced, such a gene will be in danger of extinction, as the number of individuals which it affects will again be very small. The chances that the particular individual in which a non-adaptive mutation occurs should be the ancestor of an unduly large *proportion* of a subsequently increased population are very remote ; that is, if no improvement occurs in the effect of the gene.

The extreme slowness of evolutionary progress in nature makes it exceedingly difficult to study. It is not to be expected, then, that much direct observation will be available in support of the theory just outlined. It does happen, however, that in one instance at least it has been possible to study a fluctuating population for a considerable period of time. It chanced that the changes which occurred were rather marked, and they certainly seemed to corroborate the theoretical expectations which we have been discussing.

H. D. and E. B. Ford (1930) kept an isolated colony of the butterfly *Melitœa aurinia* under observation for thirteen years. Records of its condition had been made by collectors during a previous period of thirty-six years, and preserved specimens obtained at intervals during this time were also available for comparison with each other and with the recent forms. A fairly accurate study of this particular population was therefore possible for a total period of forty-nine years.

During this time marked fluctuations in numbers occurred, which were partly due to parasitism of the larvæ. The colony was well separated from any other in the district, and confined to a very limited area : a few swampy fields from which the imagines seldom strayed even for a few yards, for they are very localized in habit and fly but weakly. It therefore formed a fairly well isolated unit.

In 1881 the species was quite abundant in this locality, and it continued to be so, but with a slight increase, until 1894, by which time it had become excessively common, the imagines occurring ' in clouds ', as the records say, during the few weeks that they are on the wing. After 1897 the numbers began to decline, and from 1906 to 1912 the species was quite scarce. From 1912 to 1920 it was extremely rare, only a few specimens being found each year, where once they could be seen in thousands. From 1920 to 1924, however, a very rapid increase took place, and from that time until 1930 it remained very abundant, with a slow, steady increase year by year.

The amount of variation was small during the first period of abundance and while the species was becoming scarce. Indeed, a constant form may be said to have existed at that time, and even small departures from it were quite infrequent. When the numbers were rapidly increasing, however, an extraordinary outburst of variation occurred. Hardly two specimens were alike and marked departures from the normal form of the species, both in size, shape, and colour, were very common. A high proportion of these were deformed in various ways ; the amount of deformity being closely correlated with the degree of variation. When the rapid increase had ceased these undesirable elements practically disappeared, and the species settled down once more to a comparatively uniform type, which, however, was recognizably distinct from that which prevailed during the first period of abundance.

The increase in variation which was witnessed in this instance was so rapid, and the changes so marked, that it is difficult to believe that the processes of genic spread and improvement here postulated were wholly responsible for them. Whatever contributing cause may have been at work, it will none the less be seen how closely the observed facts followed the course of evolutionary progress which has been suggested as possible in fluctuating populations.

The strong probability that the effects of the genes are multiple has already been discussed. This consideration may throw some light on the nature of the characters which separate local races and closely allied species. That these are sometimes entirely non-adaptive has been demonstrated, we believe successfully, by Richards and Robson (1926).

It is evident that certain genes which either initially or ultimately have beneficial effects may at the same time produce characters of a non-adaptive type, which will therefore be established with them. Such characters may sometimes serve most easily to distinguish different races or species ; indeed, they may be the only ones ordinarily available, when the advantages with which they are associated are of a physiological nature. Further, it may happen that the chain of reactions which a gene sets going is of advantage, while the end-product to which this gives rise, say a character in a juvenile or the adult stage, is of no adaptive significance. For this latter suggestion I am indebted to Mr. C. S. Elton.

J. S. Huxley (1924, 1927 a and b) has pointed out another way in which non-adaptive specific differences may arise. For he has shown that changes in absolute body-size, in themselves probably adaptive, may automatically lead to disproportionate growth in a variety of structures, such as horns and antlers in Mammalia and the appendages in Arthropoda. The effects so produced may be very striking, but, as they are the inevitable result of alteration in size, they can rarely have an adaptive significance.

It is not perhaps always recognized how complete has been the demonstration provided by the above authors that the characters available to systematists for the separation of allied species may be of a wholly non-adaptive kind. We are not justified, however, in assuming that they have therefore been established by a process of non-adaptive evolutionary change. Many of them are very invariable. An example is provided by the chitinous processes within the claspers of some male moths. These may show most constant differences in allied species ; yet the female parts are often identical with each other and quite unmodified to fit those of the male, which therefore appear almost certainly to be non-adaptive. Yet it is gravely to be doubted if the uniformity of each male type could be preserved in the absence of at least associated stabilizing selection. Even if a non-adaptive character were to be established by chance survival, it appears to the author in the highest degree improbable that it could then be maintained in a constant condition purely fortuitously.

In the instance already discussed, that of fluctuation in *Melitœa aurinia*, the distinction between the old and the new forms was a small difference in colour and marking. In the circumstances this would appear to be non-adaptive. We may, however, suspect that it was associated with an adaptive change of some more subtle nature. The strong probability that the genes which affect the colour, size, and pattern of this insect also control physiological processes in the body, is indicated by the close correlation between all the more extreme variations and deformities of various kinds.

We may now consider a problem of considerable importance and some difficulty ; that is, the existence of polymorphism in certain species in natural conditions. One of the first facts to throw any light on this subject was the demonstration by Fryer (1913) that the occurrence of the three female forms of the mimetic butterfly *Papilio polytes* is controlled by a simple Mendelian mechanism. It is now known that polymorphism is generally, but not universally, dependent upon a basis of this kind ; the castes of certain social insects may be cited as instances in which it is maintained by quite other means.

It has been shown by Fisher (1927) that the necessary condition for the establishment of polymorphism of the Mendelian type is, first, that the ratio in which the members of some allelomorphic pair occur should be in stable equilibrium. That is to say, if for any reason their proportionate numbers are disturbed, they will tend automatically to return to their original value. What this may be will depend upon the particular situation involved, but all values are possible. Secondly, that no such stable equilibrium as this could be maintained in the absence of selection. The truth of these two propositions will be evident from the following considerations.

In the absence of selection, the number of individuals in a population which possess a gene derived from a single mutation cannot greatly exceed the number of generations since its occurrence (Fisher, 1930 *b*, p. 80). In the majority of species this would require a period of time immensely greater than could possibly be allowed for the establishment of polymorphism. The presence, then, in a common species of two or more forms in anything approaching equal numbers must inevitably indicate that the spread of that dependent upon the more recent gene must have been hastened by selection. But if such selective advantage were to continue unchecked, it would result in the whole species being converted to the favoured type and in that less favoured being completely ousted. Polymorphism, then, can only be established if such selective advantage decreases and is finally reversed as the individuals which enjoy it become proportionately commoner. It must therefore be dependent upon a selective advantage balanced against some disadvantageous condition.

Two types of equilibrium, therefore, are possible. Polymorphism will result if the heterozygote possesses some physiological advantage as compared with the homozygote ; it may, for example, be more fertile. It would seem improbable, however, that such a condition as this is often maintained without other contributing factors, as improvement in the fertility of the more favourable homozygous type might be expected to take place. It may, on the other hand, be controlled by the nature of the advantage itself. Thus a Batesian mimic will progressively lose its advantage as its numbers increase relative to those of its model, until its necessarily conspicuous pattern actually becomes a danger. If polymorphism exists in such a species, the numbers of the different forms will be adjusted until each receives equal protection. Optimum proportions would thus be arrived at in any given locality, departures from which in either direction would constitute a disadvantage. In such a situation as this no form would be able to spread completely through the species. It is to be noticed that polymorphism is, in fact, common in mimetic insects.

These two forms of stabilizing action may be combined. Fryer encountered numerous sterile unions in his *polytes* crosses, and it has been pointed out by Fisher that the simplest explanation of these is a reduced fertility of the homozygous mutant types. It would appear therefore that we are here faced with a stabilizing mechanism of the ecological type, the advantages of which are in addition balanced against a state of genetic infertility. The part played by physiological agencies may further be illustrated by the polymorphism studied by Gerould (1923) in butterflies of the genus *Colias*. In the species under discussion, the males are nearly always yellow while the females may either be yellow or white ; the latter being the less numerous form. Gerould encountered great difficulty in obtaining the homozygous white type, owing to the presence of a closely-linked lethal factor. That such a character is maintained fairly commonly in nature suggests that the condition of homozygous lethality with which it is associated must be balanced by some powerful advantage. Its nature, in this instance, is in doubt ; but it will be evident from what has already been said of the multiple effects of the genes, that we need not necessarily seek it in the visible difference between the two forms.

The stable nature of the equilibrium which character-

izes polymorphic species is further indicated by the
fact that it may sometimes persist for long periods
of time. Thus the banding of certain land-snails is
inherited on simple Mendelian lines. Diver (1929)
showed that the proportion of banded and unbanded
forms in some living colonies does not differ from those
of Pleistocene age.

It is evident, however, that where stability depends
upon ecological factors, the proportions of the different
forms may vary widely in different localities. I am
much indebted to Mr. C. S. Elton for supplying me with
the information on foxes which illustrates this and other
points. The Arctic Fox (*Vulpes lagopus*) is subject to a
winter polymorphism, the individuals being either ' blue '
or white. In Kamchatka only the white type is found,
and on certain islands off the coast of Alaska only the
blue ; while on the mainland of Alaska a north-to-south
gradient in the proportion of the two occurs, the blue
being commoner in the south.

Stability may further be upset, or rather it may have
a slightly different meaning, if the species concerned is
one whose numbers are given to fluctuation. For the
whole ecological situation may be different when the
population is at its maximum and at its minimum. Elton
has studied the fluctuations which occur in the Red Fox
(*Vulpes fulva*) of North America. He finds that it is
subject in some places to a regular ten-year cycle in
numbers, with smaller irregular changes. Systematists
have divided the Red Fox into several species, but
many are characterized by a polymorphism involving
the same types : red, ' cross', and silver. The first
two are the common forms, though on Prince Edward
Island the ' cross ' type does not occur. Silver foxes
are rarer, and Elton has found that in a given
locality the proportion of this form varied over a com-

plete cycle in numbers, returning to its former value at the end of the period. In such circumstances we may suspect that stability is preserved in that the optimum proportions tend to be maintained, though these may not be the same in the various ecological situations which exist at different levels of abundance.

From what has been said of dominance it will be evident that in all types of polymorphism the hetero-zygote will come to resemble the more advantageous form, though in the homozygote this may be counter-balanced by some genetic disadvantage. Thus the white females of the genus *Colias* studied by Gerould are dominant, though they are the rarer form in nature. In ordinary circumstances we should expect an advan-tageous, and therefore dominant, gene to have spread rapidly throughout the whole species. The lethal condition of the homozygote prevents this. Similarly the mimetic forms of *Papilio polytes* are dominant to the non-mimetic. The conditions which give rise to polymorphism must in fact be very favourable for dominance modification, since the heterozygous types will be quite common in the population instead of forming a minute fraction of it, perhaps one in 10^4 or so, as they do in general. The heterozygotes will therefore be particularly quick to convert themselves to the more advantageous type.

Haldane (1930) has drawn attention to those curious instances in which polymorphism in nature is associated with close linkage, either between genes or whole chromosomes, and with the occurrence of a relatively common ' universal recessive'. To this the polymorphic forms are completely dominant, though, if allelo-morphic, they show no dominance between one another. This condition occurs in widely distinct groups, being found in the grouse locusts *Paratettix* and *Apotettix*, in land-snails such as *Helix* (*Cepœa*) *hortensis* and *nemoralis*, and in the fish *Lebistes reticulatus*. The problems presented by it have been discussed in detail by Fisher (1930 *a*) in an article of much interest.

It has already been suggested that the close linkage and frequent allelomorphism which occurs in these species is due to linkage between whole chromosomes, and that this may be accounted for by sectional translocations, the dominant genotypes being due to duplication of such translocated segments (Haldane, *l.c.*). The fact that the various polymorphic forms enjoy a selective advantage over their universal recessive may be inferred from their complete dominance. Fisher has pointed out that this is probably balanced by a deficiency in viability associated with the homozygous duplication. He has actually been able to demonstrate a significant deficiency of homozygous dominants in Nabour's extensive breeding experiments on the grouse locusts.

Fisher points out that where close linkage exists, the number of recombinations available for genic improvement is reduced. In these circumstances the genes no longer compete with their allelomorphs independently in pairs, but large systems of linked genes, or perhaps entire genotypes, come into competition as if they were a system of multiple allelomorphs. It is no longer possible for numerous genetic improvements to take place simultaneously ; they must now follow one at a time, those giving the lesser advantage always making way for those giving the greater. Many genes which confer only a small selective advantage may thus be continually crowded out, because all the available chromatin is engaged with matters of greater importance. A character involving only small selective advantages, such as colour-pattern, may thus be debarred from the

7

main method of evolutionary adaptation. This allows a duplication, or other chromosome abnormality deleterious when homozygous, to improve the colour-pattern and establish polymorphism. For the dominance of such factors could not be developed by the selection of modifiers, as these would enjoy a still lower selective advantage. Duplications, however, provide a tract of chromatin in which as heterozygotes these less important genes may be modified by selection, while they are protected from the competition of the universal recessive gene-complex.

3. Summary

It is important to decide whether or not the whole of organic inheritance is of the Mendelian type. The possible supplementary methods can be grouped under two main headings ; that inheritance may in part be purely maternal, and that, in so far as it is bi-sexual, it may to some extent depend upon elements which blend. The evidence indicates that almost all characters are determined by the nucleus, that is bi-sexually, except those responsible for the main outline of development characteristic of the phylum, class, or order to which the individual belongs. The facts are, however, by no means inconsistent with the view that even such fundamental characters as these are controlled by nuclear action. In regard to the second alternative a more definite statement can be made. The assumption of blending inheritance is not only unwarrantable in face of the experimental evidence available, but in certain instances at least it can be excluded even as a possibility.

We find that the effects of the genes may be altered by selection operating on the gene-complex. There is thus no reason to assume that when a gene first appeared its effects were similar to those which it produces to-day. The origin of the genes by mutation is therefore quite compatible with the slow and continuous course of evolution.

It is further apparent that a gene which has ultimately been selected may not have been beneficial from the outset. The fluctuation in numbers to which many species are subject provides special facilities for placing initially non-adaptive or even disadvantageous genes in a number of different gene-complexes, with which they have the opportunity of reacting in new and possibly beneficial ways. Such fluctuations may therefore enable evolution to take place more quickly.

The multiple effects of the genes allow non-adaptive characters to be established in a species through selection of associated advantages. Such characters will often serve most easily to distinguish closely allied species, the differences between which may consequently appear to be non-adaptive.

Polymorphism, of the usual Mendelian type, can only be established if the ratio in which the members of some allelomorphic pair occur is in stable equilibrium. This can only be maintained in the presence of selection ; it may be controlled in various ways. The condition of polymorphism leads to the production of dominance with special rapidity. Close linkage limits the number of combinations available for genic improvement and may result in the establishment of polymorphism of a peculiar type.

CHAPTER V

EVOLUTION IN WILD POPULATIONS

WE have seen that the Mendelian basis of heredity is in accord with the requirements of evolution, and that selection may lead to evolutionary progress in a species, not only by favouring certain characters but by an improvement in the effects of the genes themselves. It remains very briefly to discuss how a divergence can arise during this process, leading to the formation of distinct and ultimately specific types. At the outset, however, it is necessary to consider if direct evidence can be produced in support of two propositions fundamental to this purpose : first, that genes having minute advantageous effects are, in fact, spreading through wild populations ; and, secondly, that selection can act upon genes in natural conditions.

It had already been suspected by Darwin that ' wide ranging, much diffused, and common species vary most ' (*Origin of Species*, Chapter II). This acute conjecture remained unsubstantiated for nearly seventy years until verified by Fisher and Ford (1928), who undertook an investigation of the depth of pigment in the ground-colour of the fore-wings of certain night-flying moths. In thirty-five species this was sufficiently comparable to be represented on a standard colour scale ; over five thousand individuals were examined in this way. The species were classified into three groups as abundant, common, and uncommon. After applying appropriate statistical safeguards, it was found that the mean variance was greatest in the abundant species and least in those which are uncommon, the difference being over 70 per cent. ; those classified as common occupied an intermediate position. A similar result was obtained subsequently by Fisher (1937) when he made an extensive analysis of the relation between the abundance of birds and variation in the size of their eggs.

Comparisons such as these are laborious and not easily made. However, the time expended on them seems justified in view of their theoretical significance. There appear to be two reasons for regarding the variability of species as a function of their abundance, nor does it seem probable that other agencies contribute to this end. First, a large population offers a greater opportunity than a small one for the occurrence of very rare advantageous mutations, and for the establishment of the genes to which these give rise. Secondly, it can be shown that mutations producing genes of nearly neutral survival value must be excessively uncommon (Fisher, 1930c), while we cannot suppose that their frequency is related to the abundance of the species. Fisher (1937) has recently pointed out that the number of these ' neutral genes ' which any species can maintain will be nearly proportional to the logarithm of its population. That is to say, when very rare, their existence will favour but little the variance of the commoner forms which, however, can keep more of such genes in reserve. Changes in the environment may from time to time cause the effects of any of them to become slightly advantageous. The gene in question will then spread, giving rise to increased variability, reaching a maximum when it and its allelomorph are present in the population in equal numbers. We therefore reach the important conclusion that any difference in variability, when ascribable to the population level of the species concerned, will be due to those genes actually engaged in bringing about evolutionary change. Consequently, such observations demonstrate the spread in natural conditions of genes having small advantageous effects.

We may now consider evidence for the action of selection upon genetic factors in wild populations. Two examples, of rather different types, will suffice.

Gordon (1935a) released 36,000 specimens of *Drosophila melanogaster* on an estate near Totnes, in South Devon. These flies carried the gene for the recessive body-colour *ebony*, and its normal allelomorph, in equal numbers : dominant homozygotes, heterozygotes, and recessive homozygotes being distributed in a 1 : 2 : 1 ratio among them. In the late summer, 120 days after release, the flies were trapped and the proportions of the two allelomorphs were determined by breeding. The frequency of the gene for ' ebony ' (*eb*) had fallen from 50 per cent. to 11 per cent. during this period, which must have represented five or six generations. This result could be explained in one of two ways : either selection had operated against the ebony character, the wild-type condition being at an advantage in nature, or else the population had been diluted by fresh arrivals of normal individuals. It seems that the latter alternative can be excluded. The species is not indigenous in England, and any specimens which occur are brought into the country with imported fruit. The proportion of the *eb* gene was found to be the same in flies captured in different parts of the estate. This included a food store, which would represent the centre from which any imported specimens would have spread. Had these been introduced in significant numbers, they would certainly have been especially common here. Consequently, the *eb* gene would have been disproportionately rare in flies found round the store, which it was proved not to be. It is clear, therefore, that selection had operated in favour of the normal condition, although ' ebony ' is one of the most viable recessives ever encountered in *Drosophila melanogaster*. Yet, as Gordon points out, its elimination was so stringent that the observed result could not have been obtained even if all ebony flies had failed to breed. Thus it seems that, while the homozygous recessives were heavily handicapped, even the heterozygotes must have been at some small, though significant, disadvantage in nature.

The instance just described relates to the introduction of a special population into natural conditions. It may therefore be regarded as somewhat abnormal. However, there exists also evidence for the selective elimination of genetic factors to which no such criticism can be applied. For example, Gordon (1935*b*) obtained at least 14 genes recessive in operation, from 23 wild females of *D. melanogaster*, and 22 from 16 females of *D. subobscura*. Of these, only two were sex-linked, while no further sex-linked recessives appeared by raising the F1 generation from an additional 35 wild *D. melanogaster* and 81 *D. subobscura*. Now the proportion of genes showing sex-linkage should correspond with the ratio of the length of an X-chromosome compared with the sum of the lengths of each type of autosome, excluding inert regions. Judged on this basis, it is clear that sex-linked recessives are deficient in both these species. That is to say, genes are eliminated more rigorously when their disadvantageous effects are always fully expressed in half the population than when, as autosomal recessives, they are normally sheltered from selection in the heterozygous state. Though, as suggested by the previous experiment, such sheltering may not be complete, the difference between the sex-linked and autosomal conditions will, from this point of view, be sufficiently profound.

We may, therefore, accept the view that genes are subject to selection in nature, and that those having even minute advantageous effects can spread through wild populations. Accordingly we are in a position to consider by what means an approximately homogeneous population can become sub-divided into groups having recognizably distinct qualities, capable of leading to their fission as separate species.

It has long been appreciated that isolation is a necessary agent in such diversification. This may be defined as the existence of some check to the free flow of genes throughout a population. It may be due to a variety of causes.

Of these, the most widely recognized, and probably the most important, is *geographical isolation*. It should be realized that this includes not only barriers such as water or land (to terrestrial or aquatic forms respectively), or those due to altitude, but that mere distance will prevent a free interchange of hereditary material between individuals at opposite extremes even of a continuous range. Somewhat analogous to geographical isolation is *ecological isolation*. Here, forms are adapted to different habitats within the same region and, consequently, seldom meet.

A more distinct group is represented by the various types of physiological isolation, for these will often, though not always, have been initiated by the existence of geographical or ecological barriers. Among them may be mentioned *seasonal isolation*, in which the breeding periods of two groups occur at different times of year. Thus two very closely allied species of Geometrid moths, *Cidaria truncata* and *C. citrata*, seem to be kept apart by this means ; the single brood of the latter falling between the two broods of the former each year. *Sexual isolation* arises through a lack of mutual attraction between the sexes. For example, *Drosophila pseudoobscura* includes two ' physiological species ' A and B. These are identical in appearance and, though inhabiting somewhat different regions in North America, they exist together over part of their range (in Oregon and Washington). However, they are sharply separated from each other owing to the frequent failure of the females to allow cross-mating. The males, however, court either female type with equal readiness, and when pairing with the opposite one is allowed, it is always successful. The reality of the difference between the two races is shown by the fact that the F1 males are always sterile in both reciprocal crosses (Lancefield, 1929). *Reproductive isolation* consists in the existence of mechanical barriers to copulation or crossing, or in a failure of the motile gamete to reach, or to penetrate, the non-motile one. Finally, the occurrence of *hybrid sterility* must usually be regarded as the outcome of isolation, and consequent divergence, rather than an isolating mechanism in itself, save in those species which arise by polyploidy (pp. 24, 106–7).

When two populations of the same species are separated by a barrier, we may expect adaptive changes to proceed in the respective colonies. Progressive divergence may then take place between them. It will, however, be understood that all degrees may exist within any type of isolation. In consequence, populations of a species, whether continuous or discontinuous in their distribution, may achieve very diverse degrees of adjustment to the various environments of their range. Such adjustments may produce clear-cut distinctions where isolation is relatively complete. When it is less perfect, they will usually cause organisms to vary geographically or ecologically in a graded way. Some of this variation may be environmental only, but much of it is undoubtedly genetic. Until recently, no recognized terminology had been developed for the description of these gradients. However, this has now been supplied by Huxley (1938), who has proposed the general term ' cline ' for a geographical gradient in phenotypic characters. By the use of a prefix, its nature can be specified. For example, ' ecoclines ' in which species respond to successive ecological zones in their habitat, or ' geoclines ' in which they are subject to graded geographical variation extending over relatively long distances. Huxley (1939) has developed the study of clines with conspicuous success, and in a manner which should prove of great value in systematic work. We may briefly consider those aspects of his analysis which are especially relevant to our purpose. This may best be done with the help of examples.

Continuous clines are known to exist in many species. Thus the ground-colour of the Noctuid moth *Dianthoecia carpophaga* is pale yellow or white in south-east England, and becomes progressively dark towards the west and north. Now it is a remarkable fact that the general course of such clines may also be maintained throughout a discontinuous population, even when the groups into which it is sub-divided are separated by considerable barriers. This may be illustrated from the distribution of the Cole-tit (*Parus ater*) discussed by Huxley (*l.c.*). Three sub-species of this bird are distinguished in western Europe : *P. a. ater* from the Continent, *P. a. britannicus* from Britain, and *P. a. hibernicus* from Ireland. As Huxley points out, their main differences depend upon the existence in them of one major and two minor clines, running from east to west.

We need only consider the most important of these ;

a marked cline towards increase of yellow (lipochrome) pigmentation. This tinges the white parts with yellow, while those in which a moderate amount of melanin pigment is deposited become olive-buff instead of slate-grey. Irish specimens occasionally overlap the British form, but such are only found in eastern Ireland ; while specimens indistinguishable from *P. a. hibernicus* are known to occur in Britain, but only in the west (Wales). Thus, as Huxley remarks, ' this at once implies the interesting fact that the cline for yellow, though geographically interrupted by the Irish Channel, is still operative within the two groups concerned, although it is clear, as was suggested . . . on theoretical grounds, that the internal slopes are much less steep than that of the compound (intergroup) cline '.[1] Furthermore, the juvenile plumage is always more yellow than that of the adults ; but while British and Irish juveniles are indistinguishable, those from the Continent are always much less yellow.

The adaptive basis underlying this cline is obscure, but its interpretation in terms of physiological genetics seems to be evident. It has been shown by Ford and Huxley (1927) that genes may control the rate of processes in the body, the intensity of their action being correlated with an early onset of visible expression and with a high level in the final equilibrium position attained. As in many other clines, the facts in this instance can be fitted exactly into such a scheme : one in which genes control the speed of lipochrome production, together with the time at which it is first formed and the amount present in the adult.

---

[1] It will be evident that the distinction between two groups separated by a considerable barrier is likely to be greater than that between different parts of the same group, within which but little isolation exists.

We can now examine a cline whose adaptive significance is clear, so that its analysis can be carried further. Sumner (1926, 1930) studied three sub-species of the mouse *Peromyscus polionotus* from Florida. An almost white form (*P. p. leucocephalus*) occurs on Santa Rosa Island in the Gulf of Mexico. This is a narrow bank of white sand covered with exceedingly sparse vegetation. It stretches along the coast for about fifty miles and is separated from it by a narrow strait which at one place is only a quarter of a mile wide. A pale, though less extreme, form (*P. p. albifrons*) occupies a similar habitat on the shore and extends inland for nearly forty miles. It is then replaced by the dark typical form (*P. p. polionotus*), which lives still farther inland on very dark soil which persists throughout its range.

P. p. leucocephalus is uniform in appearance over the whole island on which it is found. *P. p. albifrons*, however, shows a marked cline of increasing pigmentation inland ; while the dark typical form, though practically constant in most parts of its range, exhibits a slight cline of decreasing pigmentation where it approaches the coast most nearly.

There can be no doubt that *P. p. leucocephalus* is adapted to living on white sand, on which *P. p. polionotus* is extremely conspicuous : as indeed are the lighter forms if placed on dark soil. Further, that its adaptation has been perfected by its isolation, while the less complete adjustment to similar conditions shown by *P. p. albifrons* is to be accounted for by the fact that it is not isolated from the dark, and also adaptive, inland race. The degree of pigmentation therefore bears a direct relation to the environmental gradient, while other variations, such as those in linear measurement, do not. The fact that *P. p. albifrons* extends for a considerable distance inland beyond the light soil must mean, as

Sumner concludes, that, after being differentiated on the white sand of the coastal strip, it has increased its numbers and extended its range inland on to dark soil. This would then lead to some adaptive darkening of the most inland section of the coastal form, and would contribute to the imperfect lightening of its most coastal section.

Sumner finds that these differences in colour are dependent upon a simple genetic basis. Stocks of the three sub-species failed to converge after several generations maintained in a common environment in the laboratory. Crosses between them lead to segregation in respect of intensity of pigment and, as close approximations to the original colours were recovered in fairly small F2 families, they must be controlled by quite a limited number of genes.

Data collected in the region forty miles from the coast where *P. p. albifrons* and *P. p. polionotus* meet shows that a zone of intergradation exists between these forms. They further disclose the extraordinary fact that this zone is only three miles wide. Here the cline is very pronounced. In addition, the coefficient of variability rises sharply in the centre of the narrow belt of intergradation.

Huxley (1939), who has made an illuminating analysis of this cline, points out that the remarkable condition here encountered is precisely in accord with a generalization put forward in conversation by Professor R. A. Fisher. That is to say, when two relatively large and uniform areas are separated by a region of rapid environmental change, selection will lead to the formation of a stabilized gene-complex within both of them. These will each be adjusted to the maximum degree of efficiency in their own environment. So long as the population is continuous, interbreeding will occur where they meet. But the recombinations between them will be less well adapted and harmonious than either of the two main gene-complexes, since each of these will be accurately balanced within itself. Such recombinations will therefore remain permanently restricted to a narrow zone, and will fail to spread through the population as a whole.

The manner in which selection can act upon the gene-complex has been discussed in the earlier chapters of this book. Its significance will again be appreciated here. Indeed, it is clear that the principle of stabilized gene-complexes adapted to the requirements of each region is of great importance in evolution. Of this the condition encountered in *Peromyscus polionotus* provides an excellent example illustrating, as it does, how a partial discontinuity can arise within a continuous population.

It will be evident that the establishment of such discontinuities can only be effective in the presence of some degree of isolation. This may take a variety of forms (pp. 92–3) : for instance, a geographical barrier, as that between *P. p. leucocephalus* and *albifrons*, or an environmental (or ecological) change in a region habitable throughout by the species, as between *P. p. albifrons* and *polionotus*. Where, as is usual, it depends upon selection acting on the gene-complex, the resulting modification will be a slow one.

It has already been pointed out that the occurrence of a mutation having favourable effects must be exceedingly infrequent (p. 46). Indeed, we might judge it an almost impossible event in a constant environment. For the recurrent nature of mutation would then ensure that any advantageous gene would already have been incorporated into the gene-complex. Only those which have been consistently rejected would still be appearing as mutations. But environments in nature are not constant, so that a gene unsatisfactory at one stage in the career of a species may be valuable at another. Consequently, mutations of an advantageous kind may even occur in genes having considerable effects, though this will be very rare indeed. However, they are evidently less improbable in an environment which has lately undergone a great change than in a relatively constant one The impact of civilization upon natural conditions will produce such alterations. Moreover, they will be of a far more rapid and profound kind than could ever otherwise occur apart, perhaps, from cataclysms of the most violent type : volcanic eruptions, for example.

It is not surprising, therefore, that one of the most notable evolutionary changes ever actually witnessed has been brought about by the spread in industrial areas of genes having considerable effects. This has taken place in a number of species belonging to widely distinct groups of the Lepidoptera. In some of these moths, almost the whole population has become blackish in manufacturing districts ; whereas they are normally of a comparatively pale shade, being mottled so as to resemble the bark or twigs upon which they habitually rest. In the majority of the species so affected, this extreme development of black pigment is under the control of a single gene (Ford, 1937).

Unlike the slow change to be anticipated where selection is operating on the gene-complex, the spread of these black forms has been quite rapid. Indeed, in numerous instances almost the whole population has become black over an entire industrial area in thirty or forty generations, or even less. These usually occupy a year each. So complete has been the change, that the pale forms, which were once the normal ones in such regions and remain so outside them, have reached the status of occasional varieties appearing perhaps in 1 or 2 per cent. of the population.

This phenomenon of 'industrial melanism' was first noticed in England, and it has attained its most considerable proportions there. However, it is now known on the Continent of Europe and elsewhere. Various theories have been advanced to account for it ; the most obvious relies merely upon the concept of protective coloration. It is a fact that the species involved are such as rest in fairly exposed positions and depend for protection upon a resemblance to their background. The normal pale specimens are decidedly conspicuous in the blackened countryside of manufacturing districts, where the black forms are tolerably concealed, while the reverse is true in unpolluted country. However, an explanation depending simply upon selection operating in favour of those forms best matching their surroundings fails to account for an additional, and highly remarkable, fact. That is to say, it has been shown in several species that the dark 'melanic' forms are actually hardier than the ordinary type. Thus in segregating families the ratios are biased in favour of the black specimens. Yet these have not spread widely in natural conditions, save in the neighbourhood of industrial areas ! It may be added that in the Geometrid moth *Gonodontis bidentata* the melanic form (*nigra*) can emerge at a lower temperature than the typical one. It has almost replaced the latter in the 'black country' of Lancashire and its surroundings : yet it has not spread northwards, which it appears physiologically so well adapted to do, although the species is common in the north of England and in Scotland.

On the other hand, Professor Harrison has endeavoured to show experimentally that such melanism is due to the induction of mutation, produced by salts of lead and manganese (Harrison and Garrett, 1926 ; Harrison, 1928). These substances are, in fact, present in the contaminated food eaten by the larvæ in manufacturing districts. Harrison is responsible for much valuable work on the ecology and genetics of melanic forms, but, in the opinion of the writer, he has not substantiated his view of their origin : indeed, it appears subject to grave objections.

After rearing larvæ for several generations on food impregnated with lead and manganese salts, Harrison obtained melanic specimens. If these were actually the result of mutation, the number which arose indicated that its rate must have been enormous : many times greater than that produced by short-wave radiation in *Drosophila*! The species on which he worked were *Selenia bilunaria* and *Tephrosia bistortata*, in both of which melanism is recessive. Consequently the gene responsible for it could have been brought into the cross in the heterozygous state, and Fisher (1933) points out that the controls used do not exclude this possibility. The choice of species was therefore an unfortunate one from the technical standpoint, but it does not appear to have been remarked that it has a yet more serious drawback. For, by making it, Harrison was investigating a phenomenon which seems never to have occurred : the spread and establishment in industrial districts of *recessive* melanism. In every instance with which I am acquainted, the successful melanics either have an intermediate heterozygote or are described as ' dominants '. In the latter event, further investigation shows the so-called dominance usually, and perhaps always, to be imperfect. These are the species among which it has been found that the melanics actually possess a physiological advantage. In *S. bilunaria* and *T. bistortata*, employed by Harrison in his investigations, the black

8

forms occur in nature only as rare varieties, and they are the less hardy. We may suppose that in these species melanism has been pressed into the recessive state owing to the physiological disadvantage with which it is associated.

Space does not permit of detailed comment on the improbability of induced mutation having the effects encountered in industrial melanism. That any agency should repeatedly cause the same gene, and seemingly that alone, to mutate in a species, is in direct contradiction to what is known of mutation. That it should do so in many different species, borders on the incredible : while if, alternatively, it be held that it is non-homologous genes having analogous effects which mutate, the improbability appears yet increased. However, it may be added that Hughes (1932) and Thomson and Lemche (1933) have failed to confirm Harrison's results on *Selenia bilunaria*, although they used very large numbers. This Harrison (1935) attributes to the larval mortality which they encountered, acting differentially upon the melanics ; and these he himself admits to be the less hardy in this species. It is more probably due to the absence of heterozygotes in the material with which the stocks were founded.

The theories so far advanced do not even provide a consistent interpretation of the facts which they seek to explain. I have therefore suggested that industrial melanism is due to causes of a fundamentally different kind (Ford, 1937) : that it is in fact produced by selection, but that this operates in favour not of the colour but of the physiological advantages possessed by those black forms which have spread. Further, that these have constantly appeared as rare varieties in the past, but that it has not been possible to utilize the genes responsible for them, owing to the excess melanin pro-

duction with which they are associated ; for this destroys
the concealing coloration upon which the species depend
for protection when at rest. Formerly, therefore, such
genes were unusable, and they largely remain so to-day,
except in or near industrial areas. Here, however, in
the blackened countryside melanism, as such, can at
least be considered a less serious handicap, possibly even
an asset. Furthermore, predators are fewer, so that
colour-pattern is probably not so important. In these
circumstances, the insects may be able to avail themselves of any other benefits which genes producing undue
pigmentation may confer.

It will be clear that such a view is in accord with the
circumstances of industrial melanism. I have discussed
the evidence for it elsewhere (Ford, 1937), but one
additional fact may be mentioned here. A melanic form
(*cornelseni*) of the Geometrid moth *Boarmia extensaria*
has established itself in manufacturing areas in Germany.
It has not done so in England, where the species is locally
common in the south but does not enter industrial districts. Yet *cornelseni* has actually occurred there as a
rare variety. This demonstrates two important facts :
first, industrial conditions are not required for its production and, secondly, that this form is available in England
had the species been able to make use of it. That it has
not done so may reasonably be attributed to the rural
nature of its habitat in this country.

The existence of industrial melanism evidently leads
to the formation of clines for coloration in those species
affected by it. Usually these are not abruptly stepped,
for the dark forms tend to spread in decreasing proportions as a penumbra round the polluted area where they
have established themselves. This is, of course, due to
the imperfect isolation of such ecoclines. It may also
be true in some instances that the melanic insects,

having proved successful in manufacturing districts, have extended their range outwards. The superficial parallel between this situation and that encountered in the *albifrons* form of *Peromyscus polionotus* (pp. 96–8) will be obvious.

It appears that even in normal circumstances the balance of selective agencies in respect of the genes concerned in industrial melanism is a close one. It has been pointed out by Fisher (1930*b*) that a selective advantage of 1 per cent. would, on the one hand, produce a considerable evolutionary change in one hundred generations while, on the other, it would require very precise methods to detect its existence in the course of experimental work. Yet here we are faced with a physiological advantage so considerable that it has been forced on the attention of those breeding these species, even though they were not especially looking for it. The varying ecological conditions of isolated areas may be expected sometimes to modify the normal equipoise so that a melanic form possessing such a physiological advantage can establish itself in a limited area outside industrial districts : and so it proves. Black forms of *Boarmia consonaria*, *B. punctinalis*, and *B. ribeata* are found in restricted colonies in Kent, Surrey, and Hampshire. They are confined to these localities, though all three species have a fairly wide, though non-industrial, distribution in England. That these black varieties have been demonstrated hardier than the typical forms, while, furthermore, they have not spread outside localized areas, is a fact deserving of careful attention. However, as will be realized, it is consistent with the interpretation here adopted. Also, the existence in normal circumstances of a small margin only of disadvantage over advantage in respect of industrial melanics, should make the intergrading region of the cline a fairly large one. So, too, the presence of melanism in manufacturing districts acts as a reservoir for the genes responsible for it.   Thus it should be easier now than in the past for them to establish themselves in other areas, in which the ecological balance is upset in their favour.   Such will be especially liable to arise owing to the changes consequent upon civilization.

The occurrence and establishment of melanic forms in regions outside manufacturing areas since the advent of industrial melanism has given rise to some speculation. However, it does not appear to call for additional hypotheses when the considerations here briefly outlined are born in mind.

It is clear, then, that isolation of various kinds leads to diversification.   In favourable circumstances, the forms so produced will eventually give rise to distinct species, for the independent evolution of the gene-complex which becomes possible in separate races will lead to the establishment of genetic incompatibility between them.   This will usually be slight at first, but in the end it may lead to a condition of partial, and later of complete, ' interspecific sterility ' which provides a physiological barrier, isolating the various forms more effectively than any geographical boundary.   Even at an early stage, it will ensure their continuity if brought back into the same habitat.   Once a measure of sterility has been developed between two races, their ultimate separation as species will generally be assured.

It has been pointed out that the production of distinct forms by isolation and selection is normally a slow process, but that it may be quite rapid in special circumstances, such as in industrial melanism.   So, too, the origin of new species occupies long periods of time, though, occasionally, this also may be hastened. However, circumstances exist in which it may even take place suddenly.   As already suggested (p. 24), these

are sometimes provided by the occurrence of allotetraploidy in plants. Indeed, there is good evidence that
species have repeatedly arisen in nature by this means.
Yet something more than a mere restoration of fertility
to a sterile hybrid must evidently be required to produce
a species which is not only new but a success. The
gene-complex of each of the parental forms will be
adjusted to its needs. That of the hybrid mixture
between them, being out of balance, will be less well
adjusted than either, and we should expect it to fail
in competition with them even if it becomes specific.
However, it has already been stressed (Chapter II) that
factors interact with each other to produce the characters for which they are responsible, so that there may be
found in a hybrid qualities possessed by neither of its
parental species. Indeed, the dissimilarity of the gene-
complexes brought together in a species-cross is more
likely to evoke new reactions from the genes composing
either of them than may be obtained by selection of the
gene-complex within a single species. For example, in
the Mexican Top-minnow (*Platypoecilus*), a sex-linked
factor *Sp* merely produces dominant black spotting. In
the hybrid between this and another form (*Xiphophorus*),
it gives rise to a fatal cancerous growth (Kosswig, 1929*a*
and *b*).

Here the effect of a gene in an internal environment
to which it is partly unaccustomed is unfavourable,
and this will be the most usual result in such
circumstances. Occasionally, however, it may chance
to be of an advantageous kind. Of this the rice-grass
Spartina provides a notable illustration. *S. stricta*, with
a diploid chromosome number of 56, is a native species
in England. It appears that chromosome doubling
occurred in a hybrid between this and *S. alterniflora*,
which was imported from America. The latter has a

diploid number of 70. The allotetraploid so produced therefore possesses 126 chromosomes. It is fertile, though sterile with both the parental forms, and constitutes a new species known as *S. Townsendii*. This first appeared in Southampton Water about 1870 and has since spread to other stations along the south coast of England, notably Poole Harbour, where it has multiplied greatly (Huskins, 1930). Thus it must have been at an advantage compared with its imported parent whose opportunities for gaining a footing would initially have been at least as favourable, since it was in a position to form a natural hybrid. Far more remarkable, however, is the fact that it has even proved superior to the native species. That this hybrid should actually compete successfully with both its parental forms indicates that the interaction of their two gene-complexes must have given rise to some new and superior quality.[1] We have here an outstanding instance of the importance of genetic variability of this kind, and of the sudden and successful establishment of a new species in natural conditions.

In the evolution of wild populations certain general

---

[1] Alternatively, it might be suggested that a character produced by a gene from one species may be recessive to that produced by the homologous gene from the other. Assuming the association of chromosome-pairs derived from the same source, this would lead to the disappearance of an ancestral character in the allotetraploid, in which the gene having the recessive effect would always be accompanied by that having the dominant one. It is improbable that this is the correct explanation here, for it must be supposed that the character which chances to be recessive in the hybrid is one which reduces the efficiency of the parent in which it is found. Furthermore, as the allotetraploid is at an advantage compared with *both* ancestral forms, we are forced to assume a similar set of circumstances, but working in the opposite direction, in respect of the other parental species.

principles may be discerned. Some of the more fundamental of these have now briefly been considered and illustrated by means of selected examples. It will be appreciated that in analysing them it was necessary to appeal to the propositions developed in the earlier chapters of this book.

The variability upon which selection operates is subject to the conditions of particulate inheritance, with all that this implies. Moreover, isolation of some type appears to be a requisite for diversification. Within the different groups to which it gives rise, stable gene-complexes adapted to the needs of the environment can be built up, but considerable time will be required for their adjustment. However, the spread of a single gene advantageous in special circumstances may take place rapidly in populations of an appropriate kind. Similarly, species formation will normally be a lengthy process ; yet, by means of allotetraploidy, it may even be achieved suddenly. But this method depends for its success upon the production of novel and advantageous effects by old genetic material when placed in a new setting. The establishment of a harmoniously balanced gene-complex, no less than the preservation or rejection of individual genes, must be regarded as a fundamental duty of selection.

LIST OF REFERENCES

BATESON, W., and PUNNETT, R. C. : (1905) 'A Suggestion as to the Nature of the Walnut Comb in Fowls', *Proc. Camb. Phil. Soc.*, **13**, 165–8.

—————— (1906) 'Experimental Studies in the Physiology of Heredity. Poultry', *Repts. Evoln. Comm. Roy. Soc.*, **3**, 11–16.

BOVERI, T. : (1903) 'Über den Einfluss der Samenzelle auf die Larvencharaktere der Echiniden', *Arch. f. Ent. mech.*, **16**, 340–63.

BRIDGES, C. B. : (1919) 'Specific Modifiers of Eosin Eye Color in *Drosophila melanogaster*', *J. Exp. Zool.*, **28**, 337–84.

CASTLE, W. E. : (1924) 'Some varieties of White Rabbits', *J. Hered.*, **15**, 211–19.

CHEN, SHISAN : (1928) 'Transparency and Mottling, A case of Mendelian Inheritance in the Goldfish *Carassius auratus*', *Genetics*, **13**, 434–52.

COLLINS, J. L. : (1927) 'A low temperature type of Albinism in Barley', *J. Hered.*, **18**, 331–4.

CORRENS, C. : (1909) 'Vererbungsversuche mit blass-(gelb)-grünen und buntblättrigen Sippen bei *Mirabilis jalapa*', *Zeit. f. Abst. Vererb.*, **1**, 291–329.

DEMEREČ, M. : (1926) 'Miniature a. A second frequently mutating character in *Drosophila virilis*', *Proc. Nat. Acad. Sci.*, **12**, 687–90.

—————— (1929 *a*) 'Genetic factors stimulating mutability of the miniature gamma wing character of *Drosophila virilis*', *Proc. Nat. Acad. Sci.*, **15**, 834–8.

—————— (1929 *b*) 'Changes in the rate of mutability of the mutable miniature gene of *Drosophila virilis*', *Proc. Nat. Acad. Sci.*, **15**, 870–6.

DIVER, C. : (1925) 'The Inheritance of Inverse Symmetry in *Limnœa peregra*', *J. Gen.*, **15**, 113–200.

—————— (1929) 'Fossil Records of Mendelian Mutations', *Nature*, **124**, 183.

DOBZHANSKY, Th. : (1927) 'Studies on the Manifold Effect of certain Genes in *Drosophila melanogaster*', *Zeit. f. Abst. Vererb.*, **43**, 330–88.

9   **109**

DOBZHANSKY, Th. : (1930 a) 'Cytological Map of the second Chromosome of *Drosophila melanogaster* ', *Biol. Zent.*, **50**, 671–85.

———— (1930 b) 'The Manifold Effects of the Genes Stubble and Stubbloid in *Drosophila melanogaster* ', *Zeit. f. Abst. Vererb.*, **54**, 427–57.

DOBZHANSKY, Th., and QUEAL, M. L. : (1938) 'Genetics of Natural Populations ', *Genetics*, **23**, 463–84.

DUBININ, N. P., *et al.* : (1934) 'Experimental Study of the ecogenotypes of *Drosophila melanogaster* ', *Biol. Zh. Mosk.*, **3**, 166–216.

ELTON, C. S. : (1924) 'Periodic Fluctuations in the Numbers of Animals ', *Brit. J. Exp. Biol.*, **2**, 119–63.

———— (1925) 'Plague and the Regulation of Numbers in Wild Animals ', *J. Hyg.*, **24**, 138–63.

———— (1927) '*Animal Ecology* '. London.

———— (1930) '*Animal Ecology and Evolution* '. Oxford.

FELDMAN, H. W. : (1924) 'Linkage of Albino Allelomorphs in Rats and Mice ', *Genetics*, **9**, 487–92.

FISHER, R. A. : (1927) 'On some Objections to Mimicry Theory ; Statistical and Genetic ', *Trans. Ent. Soc. Lond.*, **75**, 269–78.

———— (1928 a) 'The possible Modification of the Response of the Wild Type to Recurrent Mutations ', *Am. Nat.*, **62**, 115–26.

———— (1928 b) 'Two further Notes on the Origin of Dominance ', *Am. Nat.*, **62**, 571–4.

———— (1929) 'The Evolution of Dominance ', *Am. Nat.*, **63**, 553–6.

———— (1930 a) 'The Evolution of Dominance in certain Polymorphic Species ', *Am. Nat.*, **64**, 385–406.

———— (1930 b) '*The Genetical Theory of Natural Selection* '. Oxford.

———— (1930 c) 'The Distribution of Gene Ratios for rare Mutations ', *Proc. Roy. Soc. Edinb.*, **50**, 204–19.

———— (1933) 'On the Evidence Against the Chemical Induction of Melanism in Lepidoptera ', *Proc. Roy. Soc. B.*, **112**, 407–16.

———— (1935) 'Dominance in Poultry ', *Philos. Trans. Roy. Soc. B.*, **225**, 197–226.

———— (1937) 'The Relation between Variability and Abundance shown by the Measurements of the eggs of British Nesting Birds ', *Proc. Roy. Soc. B.*, **122**, 1–26.

———— (1938) 'Dominance in Poultry ', *Proc. Roy. Soc. B.*, **125**, 25–48.

FISHER, R. A., and FORD, E. B. : (1928) ' The Variability of Species in the Lepidoptera, with reference to Abundance and Sex ', *Trans. Ent. Soc. Lond.*, **76**, 367–84.

FORD, E. B. : (1928) ' The Inheritance of Dwarfing in *Gammarus chevreuxi* ', *J. Gen.*, **20**, 93–102.

——— (1930) ' The Theory of Dominance ', *Am. Nat.*, **64**, 560–66.

——— (1937) ' Problems of Heredity in the Lepidoptera ', *Biol. Rev.*, **12**, 461–503.

——— (1940) ' Genetic Research in the Lepidoptera ', *Ann. Eugenics*, **10**, 227–52.

FORD, E. B., and HUXLEY, J. S. : (1927) ' Mendelian Genes and Rates of Development in *Gammarus chevreuxi* ', *Brit. J. Exp. Biol.*, **5**, 112–34.

——— (1929) ' Genetic rate-factors in *Gammarus* ', *Arch. f. Ent. mech.*, **117**, 67–79.

FORD, H. D., and FORD, E. B. : (1930) ' Fluctuation in Numbers and its Influence on Variation, in *Melitœa aurinia* ', *Trans. Ent. Soc. Lond.*, **78**, 345–51.

FRYER, J. C. F. : (1913) ' An Investigation by Pedigree Breeding into the Polymorphism of *Papilio polytes* ', *Phil. Trans. Roy. Soc.*, *B.*, **204**, 227–54.

GEROULD, J. H. : (1923) ' Inheritance of White Wing Color, A Sex-Limited (Sex-Controlled) Variation in Yellow Pierid Butterflies ', *Genetics*, **8**, 495–551.

GERSHENSON, S. : (1928) ' A new Sex-ratio Abnormality in *Drosophila obscura* ', *Genetics*, **13**, 488–507.

GODLEWSKI, E. : (1906) ' Untersuchungen über die Bastardierung der Echiniden- und Crinoidenfamilie ', *Arch. f. Ent. mech.*, **20**, 579–643.

——— (1925) ' La corrélation plasmo-nucléaire et la matière vivante ', *C. R. Soc. Biol.*, *Réunion Plénière*, *Avril* 1925.

GORDON, C. : (1935 *a*) ' An experiment on a released population of *Drosophila melanogaster* ', *Am. Nat.*, **69**, 381.

——— (1935 *b*) ' An analysis of two wild Drosophila Populations ', *Am. Nat.*, **69**, 381–2.

HALDANE, J. B. S. : (1930) ' A Note on Fisher's Theory of the Origin of Dominance and on a Correlation between Dominance and Linkage ', *Am. Nat.*, **64**, 87–90.

HARRISON, J. W. H. : (1928) ' A further Induction of Melanism in the Lepidopterous Insect *Selenia bilunaria* Esp., and its Inheritance ', *Proc. Roy. Soc.* *B.*, **102**, 338–47.

HARRISON, J. W. H. : (1935) ' The Experimental Induction of Melanism, and other Effects, in the Geometrid Moth *Selenia bilunaria* Esp.', *Proc. Roy. Soc.* B., **117**, 78–92.

HARRISON, J. W. H., and GARRETT, F. C. : (1926) ' The Induction of Melanism in the Lepidoptera and its subsequent Inheritance ', *Proc. Roy. Soc.* B., **99**, 241–63.

HERSH, A. H. : (1924) ' The Effect of Temperature upon the heterozygotes in the Bar series of *Drosophila* ', *J. Exp. Zool.*, **39**, 55–71.

—— (1927) ' Temperature Effects in Reciprocal Crosses of the Bar series of *Drosophila* ', *J. Exp. Zool.*, **47**, 227–50.

HOGE, M. A. : (1915) ' The Influence of Temperature on the development of a Mendelian Character ', *J. Exp. Zool.*, **18**, 241–97.

HUGHES, A. W. McK. : (1932) ' Induced Melanism in Lepidoptera ', *Proc. Roy. Soc.*, B., **110**, 378–402.

HUSKINS, C. L. : (1930) ' The Origin of *Spartina Townsendii* ', *Genetica*, **12**, 531–8.

HUXLEY, J. S. : (1924) ' Constant Differential Growth-ratios and their significance ', *Nature*, **114**, 895–6.

—— (1927 *a*) ' Further work on Heterogonic Growth ', *Biol. Zent.*, **47**, 151–63.

—— (1927 *b*) ' Studies on Heterogonic Growth ', *J. Gen.*, **18**, 45–53.

—— (1938) ' Clines : an Auxiliary Taxonomic Principle ', *Nature*, **142**, 219–20.

—— (1939) ' Clines : an Auxiliary Method in Taxonomy ', *Bijdr. Dierk.*, **27**, 491–520.

JOHANNSEN, W. : (1903) ' *Über Erblichkeit in Populationem und in reinen Linien* '. Jena.

—— (1913) ' Mutation dans des lignées pures de haricot et discussion au sujet de la mutation en général ', *Repts.* 4*th Intern. Conf. Genet. Paris*.

KOSSWIG, C. : (1929 *a*) ' Über die veränderte Wirkung von Farbgenen des *Platypœcilus* in der Gattungskreuzung mit *Xiphophorus* ', *Z. indukt. Abstamm.-u. VererbLehre*, **50**, 63–73.

—— (1929 *b*) ' Zur Frage der Geschwulstbildung bei Gattungsbastarden der Zahnkarpfen *Xiphophorus* und *Platypœcilus* ', *Z. indukt. Abstamm.-u. VererbLehre*, **52**, 114–20.

LANCEFIELD, D. E. : (1929) ' A Genetic Study of crosses of two races or physiological species of *Drosophila obscura* ', *Zeit. f. Abst. Vererb.*, **52**, 287–317.

MacBride, E. W.: (1930) 'Embryology and Evolution', *Discovery*, **11**, 209.

Morgan, T. H.: (1915) 'The Role of the Environment in the Realization of a Sex-linked Mendelian Character in *Drosophila*', *Am. Nat.*, **49**, 385–429.

—— (1927) '*Experimental Embryology*'. New York.

——, Bridges, C. B., and Sturtevant, A. H.: (1925) 'The Genetics of *Drosophila*', *Bibl. Gen.*, **2**, 1–262.

Muller, H. J., and Mott-Smith, L. M.: (1930) 'Evidence that Natural Radioactivity is inadequate to explain the Frequency of Natural Mutations', *Proc. Nat. Acad. Sci.*, **16**, 277–85.

Nilsson-Ehle, H.: (1909) '*Kreuzungsuntersuchungen an Hafer und Weizen*'. Lund's Univ. Arsskrift.

Oliver, C. P.: (1930) 'The Effect of Varying the Duration of X-ray Treatment upon the Frequency of Mutation', *Science*, **71**, 44–6.

Painter, T. S. and Muller, H. J.: (1929) 'Parallel Cytology and Genetics of Induced Translocations and Deletions in *Drosophila*', *J. Hered.*, **20**, 287–98.

Patterson, J. T.: (1929) 'The Production of Mutation in Somatic Cells of *Drosophila melanogaster* by means of X-rays', *J. Exp. Zool.*, **53**, 327–72.

Plough, H. H.: (1917) 'The Effect of Temperature on Crossing-over in *Drosophila*', *J. Exp. Zool.*, **24**, 147–209.

Richards, O. W., and Robson, G. C.: (1926) 'The Species Problem and Evolution', *Nature*, **117**, 345–7, 382–4.

Russell, E. S.: (1930) '*The Interpretation of Development and Heredity*'. Oxford.

Schultz, W.: (1920) 'Kälteschwärzung eines Säugetieres und ihre allgemeinbiologischen Hinweise', *Arch f. Ent. mech.*, **47**, 43–75.

Stern, C.: (1929) 'Über die additive Wirkung multipler Allele', *Biol. Zent.*, **49**, 261–90.

Sturtevant, A. H.: (1915) 'A Sex-linked Character in *Drosophila repleta*', *Am. Nat.*, **49**, 189–92.

—— (1921 a) 'The North American Species of *Drosophila*', *Carnegie Inst. Wash.*, publ. **301**, pp. 150.

—— (1921 b) 'Genetic Studies on *Drosophila simulans*', *Genetics*, **6**, 43–64.

Sumner, F. B.: (1926) 'An Analysis of Geographic Variation in Mice of the *Peromyscus polionotus* Group from Florida and Alabama', *J. Mamm.*, **7**, 149–84.

SUMNER, F. B. : (1930) ' Genetic and Distributional Studies of three sub-species of *Peromyscus* ', *J. Gen.*, **23**, 275–376.

SUTTON, W. S. : (1902) ' On the Morphology of the Chromosome Group in *Brachystola magna* ', *Biol. Bull.*, **4**, 24–39.

THOMSEN, M. and LEMCHE, H. : (1933) ' Experimente zur Erzielung eines erblichen Melanismus bei dem Spanner *Selenia bilunaria* Esp.', *Biol. Zbl.*, **53**, 541–60.

TIMOFÉEFF-RESSOVSKY, N. W. : (1927 *a*) ' A Reverse Geno-variation in *Drosophila funebris* ', *Genetics*, **12**, 125–7.

——— (1927 *b*) ' Studies on the Phenotypic Manifestation of Hereditary Factors ', *Genetics*, **12**, 128–98.

——— (1929) ' The Effects of X-rays in producing Somatic Genovariations of a Definite Locus in different directions in *Drosophila melanogaster* ', *Am. Nat.*, **63**, 118–24.

WEXELSEN, H. : (1928) ' Two new Mutant Characters on the Spermathecæ of the females of *Drosophila melanogaster* ', *Genetics*, **13**, 389–400.

WINGE, Ö. : (1927) ' The Location of eighteen Genes in *Lebistes reticulatus* ', *J. Gen.*, **18**, 1–43.

WRIGHT, S. : (1929 *a*) ' Fisher's Theory of Dominance ', *Am. Nat.*, **63**, 274–9.

——— (1929 *b*) ' The Evolution of Dominance ', *Am. Nat.*, **63**, 556–61.

GLOSSARY

Agouti. The brownish colour produced by hairs which are banded alternately with yellow and black pigment.

Allelomorphs. Genes occupying identical loci in homologous chromosomes.

Autosome. Any chromosome other than a sex-chromosome.

Back-cross. A mating between a heterozygote and a homozygote.

Batesian Mimicry. The resemblance of a palatable to a distasteful species for protective purposes.

Blastula. The stage when the embryo is a hollow sphere of cells with no opening.

Chromatids. The two bodies produced by the longitudinal splitting of the chromosomes preparatory to nuclear division. They become the daughter chromosomes of the two resulting cells.

Chromatin. A deeply staining constituent of the nucleus. The chromosomes take up this substance when dividing.

Chromosome. One of the deeply staining paired structures which appear in the nucleus during its division. They are present in a constant number in each species and carry the genes.

Cleavage. The segmentation of the egg by which the cells of the embryo are formed.

Correlation. The study of simultaneous variation.

Coupling. The association together in linkage of the two dominant or the two recessive characters produced by different pairs of factors (compare Repulsion).

Crossing-over. An interchange of blocks of genes between the members of a chromosome pair.

Cytology. The study of cell structure.

Cytoplasm. The living substance of the cell, excluding the nucleus.

Diploid cells. Those having the two members of each chromosome pair.

Dominant. A gene which obscures the action of its allelomorph (the recessive) when present with it in the heterozygous state.

Ecology. The relation of living organisms to their environment.

Environmental variation. Variation produced by changes in the environment (compare genetic variation).

F1. The first filial generation ; the offspring of a given mating.

F2. The second filial generation ; the grandchildren of a given mating.

Factor. See ' Gene '.

Factor-pair. See ' Gene '.

Gametes. Reproductive cells of either sex. In higher animals these are the sperms and ova, while in higher plants they are enclosed in the pollen grains and ovules respectively.

Gastrula. A stage in the development of multi-cellular animals when the embryo consists of a two-layered sac.

Gastrulation. The formation of the gastrula.

Gene. An hereditary unit which controls the appearance of definite characters. The genes are paired and are carried in the paired chromosomes, where they are situated at definite loci.

Gene-complex. The interacting system produced by the whole of the genetic factors of an organism. These combine to make an internal environment in which any given factor must operate.

Gene mutation. A change in a genetic factor.

Genetics. The study of variation and heredity.

Genetic factor. See ' Gene '.

Genetic variation. Variation produced by changes (recombinations or mutations) in the genes (compare environmental variation).

Genotype. An animal judged by its genetic constitution (compare Phenotype).

Haploid cells. Those with one member only of each type of chromosome, as the reproductive cells.

Heterogametic sex. That with dissimilar sex-chromosomes.

Heteroploids. Individuals which contain a chromosome too few or too many.

Heterozygote. An individual in which the members of a given pair of genes are dissimilar.

Homogametic sex. That with similar sex-chromosomes.

Homologous chromosomes. The members of the same chromosome-pair.

Homozygote. An individual in which the members of a given pair of genes are of similar nature.

Leptotene stage. An early stage in the prophase of

meiosis in which the chromosomes first appear as long thin threads.

Linkage. The tendency for certain genes to remain together instead of assorting independently, because they are carried in the same chromosome.

Locus. The position occupied by a gene on a chromosome.

Maturation. The period during which the development of the gametes is completed. It includes meiosis.

Meiosis. The occurrence of two divisions of the nucleus with but one division of the chromosomes. These are the last divisions which the cells forming the gametes undergo, so that the gametes themselves receive one member only of each chromosome-pair. Crossing-over takes place in the prophase of the first meiosis.

Mesenchyme. Part of the middle layer of higher animals, which arises in the embryo in the form of wandering cells.

Mimicry. The resemblance of one species to another for protective purposes.

Modifying factors. These modify the characters produced by other genes. They may be without effect by themselves.

Multiple allelomorphs. Genes produced by a number of mutations of different nature at the same locus.

Multiple factors. Genes which have a similar effect, and reinforce each other.

Mutation. The inception of a heritable variation.

Nucleus. A specialized part of the protoplasm within all typical cells. It is essential for the life of the cell and is accurately halved when division occurs.

P1. The first parental generation; the individuals of the generation which are mated to produce a given cross.

Parthenogenesis. The development of an egg without fertilization.

Phenotype. An animal judged by its appearance (compare Genotype).

Plastids. Bodies in the cytoplasm of plants, which multiply by fission and are distributed irregularly at cell division.

Polymorphism. The occurrence of several forms of the same species together in a common environment.

Polyploidy. A condition in which more than two members of the chromosome-pairs are present in an organism.

Prophase. The stage preparatory to cell division when, at the first meiosis, the chromosome-pairs conjugate with each other and the chromatids resulting from them interchange material.

Protoplasm. The living substance of an organism.

Pure-line. The descendants of a single self-fertilized individual homozygous for all its factors.

Recessive. A gene whose action is obscured by its allelomorph (the dominant) when present with it in the heterozygous state.

Repulsion. The association together in linkage of the dominant character produced by one factor-pair and the recessive produced by another (compare Coupling).

R2 generation. The offspring of a ' back-cross '.

Segregation. The recovery of the original types in definite proportions in subsequent generations, when individuals exhibiting contrasted characters have been crossed.

Sex-chromosomes. The X and Y chromosomes.

Sex-controlled inheritance. Characters which can only be manifested in one or the other sex. The genes producing them may be carried either in the sex-chromosomes or in the autosomes.

Sex-linked factors. Those carried in the X-chromosomes.

Somatic mutation. Mutation taking place in the body cells instead of in those which form the gametes.

Spermatheca. An organ present in certain female animals, in which the sperm received from the male is stored.

X-chromosome. The chromosome carrying the factors which control sex determination.

Y-chromosome. The partner of the X-chromosome in one of the two sexes. It contains but few genes and, in general, does not control sex determination.

Zygote. The first cell of a new individual, produced by the fusion of the gametes. In higher animals and plants it is the fertilized ovum and ovule respectively.

INDEX

119